revise
GCSE
Mathematics:
Intermediate Level

Sheila Hunt and Philip Hooper

with Tony Buzan

Hodder & Stoughton

A MEMBER OF THE HODDER HEADLINE GROUP

C000132591

ISBN 0 340 66383–9

First published 1997
Impression number   10 9 8 7 6 5 4 3 2 1
Year   2001 2000 1999 1998 1997

The 'Teach Yourself' name and logo are registered trade
marks of Hodder & Stoughton Ltd.

Designed and produced by Gecko Ltd, Bicester, Oxon
Printed in Great Britain for Hodder & Stoughton
Educational, a division of Hodder Headline Plc,
338 Euston Road, London NW1 3BH by Scotprint Ltd,
Musselburgh, Scotland.

Mind Maps: Philip Chambers
Illustrations: Karen Donnelly, Andrea Norton,
 Mike Parsons, John Plumb, Chris Rothero
Cover design: Amanda Hawkes
Cover illustration: Paul Bateman

Contents

Roll up! Roll up!

To help you achieve that longed-for grade, we have great pleasure in introducing:

 Ringo, our ringmaster, who will whip you safely past the

 banana skins – those aspects of Mathematics that seem designed to bring you down.

He is aided and abetted by an amazing assortment of astonishing and astounding acts, including:

 Gaynor Mark, whose down-to-earth dictionary defines difficult mathematical gobbledegook in sane, simple English,

 Willie Droppitt, who will show you how to juggle formulae with ease,

 the X-traordinary, X-ceptional X-Direct acrobats who, with their friend the relaxed, rational Ray Showroola will teach you a sense of proportion,

 Hans Zoff, our Bavarian conjuror – marvel as his magical mastery makes algebraic anxieties all vanish into thin air – and last, but by no means least:

 Madam Attix Says:

Madam Attix, our gipsy fortune-teller. Note well her wise sayings. She foretells that your predicted D or E could become a C, whilst a C might well turn into a B.

Revision made easy

The four pages that follow contain a gold mine of information on how you can achieve success both at school and in your exams. Read them and apply the information, and you will be able to spend less, but more efficient, time studying, with better results. If you already have another *Hodder & Stoughton Revision Guide*, skim-read these pages to remind yourself about the exciting new techniques the books use, then move ahead to page 1.

This section gives you vital information on how to remember more *while* you are learning and how to remember more *after* you have finished studying. It explains

how to use special techniques to improve your memory

how to use a revolutionary note-taking technique called Mind Maps that will double your memory and help you to write essays and answer exam questions

how to read everything faster while at the same time improving your comprehension and concentration

All this information is packed into the next four pages, so make sure you read them!

Your *amazing* memory

There are five important things you must know about your brain and memory to revolutionise your school life.

1 **how your memory ('recall') works *while* you are learning**

2 **how your memory works *after* you have finished learning**

3 **how to use Mind Maps – a special technique for helping you with all aspects of your studies**

4 **how to increase your reading speed**

5 **how to zap your revision**

1 Recall during learning – the need for breaks

When you are studying, your memory can concentrate, understand and remember well for between 20 and 45 minutes at a time. Then it *needs* a break. If you carry on for longer than this without one, your memory starts to break down! If you study for hours non-stop, you will remember only a fraction of what you have been trying to learn, and you will have wasted valuable revision time.

So, ideally, *study for less than an hour*, then take a five- to ten-minute break. During the break listen to music, go for a walk, do some exercise, or just daydream. (Daydreaming is a necessary brain-power booster – geniuses do it regularly.) During the break your brain will be sorting out what it has been learning, and you will go back to your books with the new information safely stored and organised in your memory banks. We recommend breaks at regular intervals as you work through the *Revision Guides*. Make sure you take them!

2 Recall after learning – the waves of your memory

What do you think begins to happen to your memory straight *after* you have finished learning something? Does it immediately start forgetting? No! Your brain actually *increases* its power and carries on remembering. For a short time after your study session, your brain integrates the information, making a more complete picture of everything it has just learnt. Only then does the rapid decline in memory begin, and as much as 80 per cent of what you have learnt can be forgotten in a day.

However, if you catch the top of the wave of your memory, and briefly review (look back over) what you have been revising at the correct time, the memory is stamped in far more strongly, and stays at the crest of the wave for a much longer time. To maximise your brain's power to remember, take a few minutes and use a Mind Map to review what you have learnt at the end of a day. Then review it at the end of a week, again at the end of a month, and finally a week before the exams. That way you'll ride your memory wave all the way to your exam – and beyond!

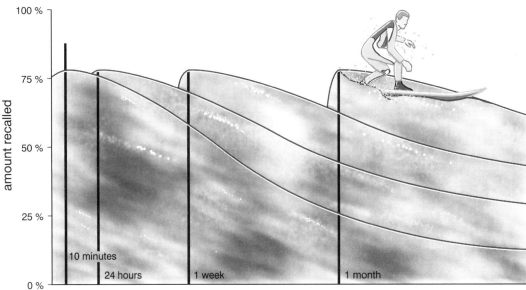

amount recalled — review time

- 100 %
- 75 %
- 50 %
- 25 %
- 0 %

10 minutes
24 hours
1 week
1 month

Amazing as your memory is (think of everything you actually do have stored in your brain at this moment) the principles on which it operates are very simple: your brain will remember if it (a) has an image (a picture or a symbol); (b) has that image fixed and (c) can link that image to something else.

3 The Mind Map® – a picture of the way you think

Do you *like* taking notes? More importantly, do you like having to go back over and learn them before exams? Most students I know certainly do not! And how do you take your notes? Most people take notes on lined paper, using blue or black ink. The result, visually, is *boring*! And what does your brain do when it is bored? It turns off, tunes out, and goes to sleep! Add a dash of colour, rhythm, imagination, and the whole note-taking process becomes much more fun, uses more of your brain's abilities, *and* improves your recall and understanding.

A Mind Map mirrors the way your brain works. It can be used for note-taking from books or in class, for reviewing what you have just studied, for revising, and for essay planning for coursework and in exams. It uses all your memory's natural techniques to build up your rapidly growing 'memory muscle'.

You will find Mind Maps throughout this book. Study them, add some colour, personalise them, and then have a go at drawing your own – you'll remember them far better! Put them on your walls and in your files for a quick-and-easy review of the topic.

How to draw a Mind Map

- Start in the middle of the page with the page turned sideways. This gives your brain the maximum room for its thoughts.

- Always start by drawing a small picture or symbol. Why? Because a picture is worth a thousand words to your brain. And try to use at least three colours, as colour helps your memory even more.

- Let your thoughts flow, and write or draw your ideas on coloured branching lines connected to your central image. These key symbols and words are the headings for your topic. The Mind Map at the top of the next page shows you how to start.

- Then add facts and ideas by drawing more, smaller, branches on to the appropriate main branches, just like a tree.

- Always print your word clearly on its line. Use only one word per line. The Mind Map at the foot of the

next page shows you how to do this.

- To link ideas and thoughts on different branches, use arrows, colours, underlining, and boxes.

How to read a Mind Map

- Begin in the centre, the focus of your topic.

- The words/images attached to the centre are like chapter headings: read them next.

- Always read out from the centre, in every direction (even on the left-hand side, where you will have to read from right to left, instead of the usual left to right).

Using Mind Maps

Mind Maps are a versatile tool – use them for taking notes in class or from books, for solving problems, for brainstorming with friends, and for reviewing and revising for exams – their uses are endless! You will find them invaluable for planning essays for coursework and exams. Number your main branches in the order in which you want to use them and off you go – the main headings for your essay are done and all your ideas are logically organised!

4 Super speed reading

It seems incredible, but it's been proved – the faster you read, the more you understand and remember! So here are some tips to help you to practise reading faster – you'll cover the ground more quickly, remember more, *and* have more time for revision!

★ Read the whole text (whether it's a lengthy book or an exam paper) very quickly first, to give your brain an overall idea of what's ahead and get it working. (It's like sending out a scout to look at the territory you have to cover – it's much easier when you know what to expect!) Then read the text again for more detailed information.

★ Have the text a reasonable distance away from your eyes. In this way your eye/brain system will be able to see more at a glance, and will naturally begin to read faster.

★ Take in groups of words at a time. Rather than reading slowly and 'carefully' read faster, more enthusiastically. Your comprehension will rocket!

★ Take in phrases rather than single words while you read.

★ Use a guide. Your eyes are designed to follow movement, so a thin pencil underneath the lines you are reading, moved smoothly along, will 'pull' your eyes to faster speeds.

5 Helpful hints for exam revision

Start to revise at the beginning of the course. Cram at the start, not the end and avoid 'exam panic'!

Use Mind Maps throughout your course, and build a Master Mind Map for each subject – a giant Mind Map that summarises everything you know about the subject.

Use memory techniques such as mnemonics (verses or systems for remembering things like dates and events, or lists).

Get together with one or two friends to revise, compare Mind Maps, and discuss topics.

And finally...

● *Have fun while you learn* – studies show that those people who enjoy what they are doing understand and remember it more, and generally do it better.

● *Use your teachers* as resource centres. Ask them for help with specific topics and with more general advice on how you can improve your all-round performance.

● *Personalise your **Revision Guide*** by underlining and highlighting, by adding notes and pictures. Allow your brain to have a conversation with it!

Your brain is an amazing piece of equipment – learn to use it, and you, like thousands of students before you will be able to master your maths with ease. The more you understand and use your brain, the more it will repay you!

What's wrong with maths?

How often have you said …

1 ✗ *Maths is boring.*

✔ Our book is different. We can't absolutely guarantee not to bore you, but at least we'll try not to.

2 ✗ *It has lots of long, strange words which I don't understand.*

✔ It may amaze you, but maths can be simple and we promise to explain what we mean in ordinary, plain English.

3 ✗ *You have to learn hundreds of formulae and methods and I can't remember them.*

✔ You don't have to learn masses of material, and we've thought up all sorts of original ways to help you remember the bits which you just must know.

4 ✗ *It takes up all your spare time, and I can think of loads of things I'd rather do.*

✔ Our easy methods and short cuts should help you save time, effort and worry.

Just imagine – you can spend even more time lounging around doing nothing and end up with a better grade!

5 ✗ *Why didn't I buy this book before?*

✔ You win! Even we don't have all the answers. Still, better late than never!

Keep this under your hat!

If you skim through chapters 1 and 2, you'll find most of our secrets revealed there and *you could learn enough in those few pages to push your marks up a grade!*

After that, though, it's up to you, and you can work through the rest of this book in any order you like. For instance, if Trigonometry always trips you up, or you stumble over Statistics, you may want to tackle those chapters next. It doesn't matter.

However you choose to use this book, though, we hope that you'll find it easy to follow, and that our circus and fairground characters will help you make the grade.

Good luck!

Important note!

Sometimes you may be surprised to find that your answer is just slightly different from the one given – especially if you have used a calculator to work it out. Don't worry – this can happen when calculators are used. It all depends when you round your answers.

If you carry out a long string of calculations on your calculator, your answer will not be rounded until the very end. However, if you make lots of shorter calculations, you are likely to round each time. This will give you a slightly different answer. The examiner will understand this.

Always read the question carefully and follow the instructions exactly, just in case you are told at which points to round your answers.

Sheila Hunt and Philip Hooper

The Mathematical Aid Circus

THE MATHS-AID CIRCUS

X-Direct Acrobats

Ringo

Karate Ken

Noel Droppitt

Hans Zoff

Kenny Droppitt

Willie Droppitt

Ray Showroola

Ronnie Mauver

Bernie Stung

Don't slip on the banana skins

Box Crusher

Gaynor Marks Dictionary

Madam Attix

HEED THE GIPSY'S WARNING

This book can seriously affect your performance by pushing your mark up a grade or two.

WITH FULL SUPPORTING CAST
Eva Rupp Honor Dyatt
Ivanitch & his amazing fleas Candida Pinion
Delia Cardswright and lots, lots more!

DINO

COSTAS

1

Proportion, percentages and ratio

How many of these coconuts would you shy away from?

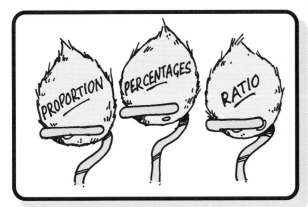

By the end of this chapter, thanks to that death-defying duo, the X-Direct Acrobats, our very own ratio expert, Ray Showroola, and a huge supporting cast, these problems will be a thing of the past!

Meet the ringmaster

Ringo the ringmaster is the first person you will meet in this chapter. He's a mine of useful information and he'll keep you on the right track. Look out for his helpful tips and reminders.

preview

By the end of this chapter you will be able to:

- answer questions on direct and inverse proportion

- find one number as a percentage of another

- find a given percentage of a number

- increase or decrease a price or amount by a given percentage

- calculate the percentage discount on a price

- calculate the VAT-inclusive price of an article, given the pre-VAT price

- calculate the pre-VAT price, given the VAT-inclusive price

- divide a given number or amount in a given ratio

- calculate individual shares of a number or amount divided in a given ratio

- state ratios in their lowest terms

- state ratios in the form 1 : *n* or *n* : 1

- work out the lengths involved in scale drawing

How much do you know already?

Exercise 1.1

1 1 kilogram is approximately 2.2 pounds (1 kg ≈ 2.2 lbs).
   a) Big Hilda Klime weighs 75 kg. How much is that in pounds?
   b) 14 pounds = 1 stone. Express your answer to part **a)** in stones and pounds.
   c) A man weighs 12 st 8 lbs. Express this in kg.

2 What is 40% of 60?

3 A pie chart is drawn to represent 300 members of the audience. How many degrees represent 80 members?

4 Two litres of a solution contain 850 grams of a chemical.
   a) How many litres would contain 1500 g?
   b) How many grams are there in 3.3 litres? Give your answer to the nearest hundred grams.

5 In a test, a student scored 45 out of a possible 70 marks. What percentage was this?

6 The plan of a new house and garden is drawn, using a scale of 1 : 25.
   a) The length of the kitchen as drawn on the plan is 15 cm. What is its actual length, in metres?
   b) The actual garden is 12.5 metres long. How long will it be on the plan?

7 The lengths of the labels of two jars are in the ratio of 5 : 2.
   a) If the larger label is 8 cm wide, how wide is the smaller?
   b) If the smaller label is 5 cm high, find the height of the larger.

8 Mike Harr bought a van for £9500 and sold it a year later for £7800. Find its depreciation as a percentage of the cost price.

Answers

8 18%
7 a) 3.2 cm **b)** 12.5 m
6 a) 3.75 m **b)** 50 cm
5 64%
4 a) 3.53 litres
   b) 1402.5 g = 1400 g to the nearest hundred grams
3 96°
2 24
1 a) 165 lbs **b)** 11 stone 11 pounds **c)** 80 kg

How did you get on?

All of them right?

Well done! Questions of this type are extremely common at Intermediate level. If you found them easy, you probably have methods which work well for you, and you don't need to change them. However, you may find that we can show you some shortcuts that could save you valuable minutes in the exam, so it's worth looking through our methods which we show you below. You just might pick up a tip or two.

Most questions right, but a few blunders?

You are just the sort of person for whom this chapter was written. With the help of X-Direct or Ray Showroola, you should score 100% next time.

Don't even ask?

Don't despair. Just work through this chapter and you'll see just how easy it is to score 100%!

Proportion

Introducing our fabulous X-Direct Acrobats

Here they are, in a really easy example.

Example 1.1 – A Really Easy Example!

Five books cost £15. Find the cost of seven books.

This is probably the method you used in the past.

   5 books cost £15
   1 book costs £15 ÷ 5 = £3
   7 books cost £3 × 7 = £21

Solution

Using the X-Direct method

Step 1

Set out the information in a table.

	Books	Cost (£)
What does the question tell me?	5	15
What do I need to know?	7	

Make sure you put the numbers under the right heading!

Step 2

Books   Cost (£)

5 ⤫ 15
7

Draw in the diagonal X as shown.

The acrobat with two numbers is Times.

The other acrobat, with one number, is Divide.

Just Times the two, Divide by the other.

Books   Cost (£)

5 ⤫ 15
7

Cost of 7 books $= \dfrac{7 \times 15}{5} = 21$

Seven books cost £21.

Once you get the hang of this, it's really quick and easy, as you'll discover when you see it in action.

Example 1.2

A box of chocolates was bought in the USA for $4.58, when the exchange rate was £1 = $1.42. Give the cost in English currency to the nearest penny.

Solution

	£	Cost $
What does the question tell me?	1	1.42
What do I need to find?		4.58

(with X-Direct diagonal cross between 1, 1.42, 4.58)

Using X-Direct, you can see that the calculation is

$\dfrac{1 \times 4.58}{1.42} = £3.23$

Since you are multiplying by 1, you can of course leave it out of your written working without affecting the answer, but many people prefer to write everything in until they get used to X-Direct.

*Tip! Try to get into the habit of making a rough estimate **before** you hit the calculator buttons, just to give you some idea of what answer to expect.*

Example 1.3

Paul E. Payde worked for 42 hours and received £48.30. How much would he receive for working 20 hours at the same rate?

Solution

Estimate: 20 is about half of 42, so he should receive about £24.

	Hours	£
What does the question tell me?	42	48.30
What do I need to know?	20	

(with X-Direct diagonal cross)

Amount $= \dfrac{20 \times 48.30}{42} = £23.00$

Example 1.4 – Using X-Direct more than once

1 litre ≈ 1.75 pints

(≈ *means 'approximately equals'*)

8 pints = 1 gallon

How many litres are approximately equal to 30.5 gallons?

Solution

You need to work backwards on this one.

	pints	gallons
What do I know?	8	1
What must I find?		30.5

(with X-Direct diagonal cross)

$\dfrac{8 \times 30.5}{1} = 244$ pints

Now consider the relationship between pints and litres.

	pints	litres
What do I know?	1.75	1
What must I find?	244	

$$30.5 \text{ gallons} \approx \frac{244 \times 1}{1.75} = 139.4 \text{ litres}$$

Now you try your luck!

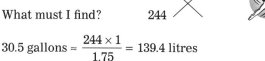
Exercise 1.2

1 a) 3.5 m of tape cost £4.20. What would 8 m cost?
   b) How much would you get for £15?

2 30 cm ≈ 1 foot
   3 feet = 1 yard
   1760 yards = 1 mile

   How many metres are approximately equal to 1 mile?

3 Ivanitch the flea tamer buys honey for his fleas in different sized pots. The larger jar weighs 850 grams and costs £4.50 and the smaller costs £1.75 for 300 grams.
   a) Which is better value and why? Show your working.
   b) Why might Ivanitch's mother choose the other size instead?

Answers

1 a) £9.60 **b)** 12.5 m
2 1584 m
3 He can buy 188 g for £1.00 if he buys the larger size. He gets 171 g for £1.00 if he buys the smaller size. The larger is better value, but his mother might buy the smaller if she did not use much honey.

Meet Gaynor Mark
It's time for you to meet another character who features widely in this book. Gaynor Mark has written a very useful dictionary which translates English into the weird and wonderful language of

ENGLISH -
MαTHS
DICTIONARY

by
Gaynor
Mark

Maths exams. This makes it much easier for candidates to understand what the question is asking, and so it gives them a better chance of actually answering it.

Whenever you see this sign, you know that Gaynor Mark is about to give you a useful hint.

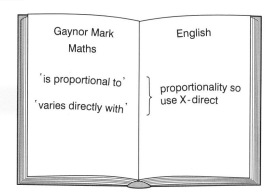

Gaynor Mark Maths	English
'is proportional to' 'varies directly with'	proportionality so use X-direct

TAKE A BREAK

This is a good point to take a break.

When you come back, look again at the principles of X-Direct. Start to make a list of situations when you could use the technique. You will be surprised how often it crops up.

Avoiding pitfalls
We have used the symbol of the banana skin to point out potential hazards which could trip you up. Whenever you see the banana skin you know there is something that could cause you a problem. It's a warning to be careful and to try to avoid common mistakes. Its first appearance in this book is to help you distinguish X-Direct problems from those involving inverse proportion.

Inverse proportion

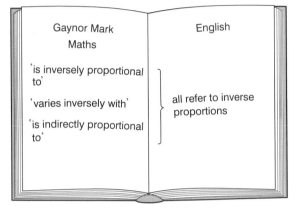

Gaynor Mark Maths	English
'is inversely proportional to'	
'varies inversely with'	all refer to inverse proportions
'is indirectly proportional to'	

A problem involving inverse proportion is one of the very rare cases where X-Direct must *not* be used.

Example 1.5

A journey takes 6 hours at 40 km/h. How long does it take at 80 km/h?

Common sense tells you that the faster you go, the less time you take, so you must use ***inverse proportion*** *(i.e. one variable gets bigger as the other gets smaller and vice versa). X-Direct only applies to questions where both variables increase at the same rate, or both decrease at the same rate.*

Solution

Multiply what you are given $\qquad 6 \times 40 = 240$

And then

Divide by the other number. $\qquad 240 \div 80 = 3$

The journey takes 3 hours.

Introducing Madam Attix

Madam Attix is a wise old woman. Her sayings will help you remember formulae and rules.

> **Madam Attix Says:**
> *Inverse proportion can drive you MAD!*
> **M**ultiply **A**nd then **D**ivide.

Caution!

Do not use X-Direct for inverse proportion.

Inverse proportion questions are not nearly as common, but we have inserted them here, so that you don't muddle them with X-Direct.

Exercise 1.3

1 If Dinah Tate and four friends share the bill at a restaurant, the cost per head is £24.00. How much should each person pay if the cost is shared among eight people?

2 Andy Chapterno and two other odd-job people can put up the Big Top in three hours. How long would six people take?

Answers

1 £15.00
2 1.5 hours

TAKE A BREAK

Now's the time for a break! You probably feel you need it. Don't make it too long, though, because we still have to tackle percentages.

Percentages

Percentages feature very prominently throughout Intermediate level papers, so this section could help you pick up some useful marks. If you have a method which works for you, then by all means, continue to use it. However, the mere fact that you are reading this section probably means that you are having problems, so try X-Direct!

Percentages using X-Direct

Important! One hundred per cent, or 100%, means the whole, original or total amount.

This, unbelievably, is all you have to know to use this method.

Type 1: Finding the percentage of a number

Example 1.6

What is 30% of £200?

Solution

100% is the original amount of £200.

It is the amount of money which equals 30% of £200 that we need to know.

Pounds (£)   Percentage (%)
200   100
              30

Using X-Direct:

$$\frac{200 \times 30}{100} = 60$$

So your answer, as it should be in the pounds column, is £60.

Type 2: Expressing one number as a percentage of another

Example 1.7

In a fairground survey, 25 stallholders, out of 125 who were asked, said that they were running their stalls at a loss. Express this as a percentage.

Solution

100% refers to the total number of people asked, i.e. 125.

We need to find 25 as a percentage of 125.

People   Percentage (%)
125   100
25

Using X-Direct:

$$\frac{25 \times 100}{125} = 20$$

As this answer would go in the percentage column, the answer is 20%.

Example 1.8

Stew Pidd bought a radio for £80.00 and sold it again for £60.00. Find the percentage loss.

Solution

Start by finding the actual loss.
(i.e. £80.00 – £60.00 = £20.00)

	£	Percentage %
Cost	£80.00	100
Loss	£20.00	

$$\text{Percentage loss} = \frac{20 \times 100}{80}$$

$$= 25\%$$

Type 3: When the figure that you are given does not refer to 100%

Example 1.9

Ivor Bargin buys a camera. The price is reduced by 20%, and it is discounted by £7.50. Find the original price.

Solution

The original price is 100%.

Percentage (%)   Pounds (£)
100
20   7.50

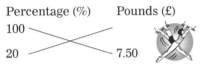

Using X-Direct: $\dfrac{100 \times 7.50}{20} = 37.5$

The answer is £37.50 (not £37.5 – money is never written like this!).

Can you see that it does not matter where the gap in the table is, as long as you keep the numbers in the correct columns, and the numbers that relate to each other next to each other?

Example 1.10

The price of a camera is reduced by 25% to £30. Find its original price.

Solution

This question is practically the same as the one before, but is worded slightly differently. This time the price after the discount has been given, rather than the discount itself.

If 25% has been taken off the original of 100%, then we have 75% left. So £30 relates to 75%.

Pounds (£)   Percentage (%)
30   75
             100

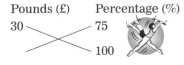

Using X-Direct: $\dfrac{30 \times 100}{75} = 40$

So the original price was £40.00.

Exercise 1.4

1 As an experiment to encourage larger audiences, the price of all tickets to the circus is reduced by 15%. If the original price of a ticket was £5.70, find the new price.

2 In an audience of 240 people, 108 were children.
   a) What percentage of the audience were children?
   b) What percentage were adults?

3 Mark M. Upp increased the site rent for the fair by 20% one year. If the new rent is £300, find the original charge.

Answers

3 £250
2 a) 45% **b)** 55%
1 £4.85

VAT questions

At the time of writing this book, VAT is 17.5%. This is a tax put on most items that you would buy in the shops. VAT questions are very common in exams.

Adding on VAT

Example 1.11

The pre-VAT price of a toy is £58.40. Find the price including VAT.

Solution

There are two ways of solving this problem: either work out 17.5% and add it on to the original price, or use the complete 'VAT-inclusive' percentage, which will be 100% +17.5% = 117.5%.

Method 1

Price (£)   Percentage (%)
58.40   100
            17.5

VAT = $\dfrac{58.40 \times 17.5}{100} = 10.22$

The price including VAT = £58.40 + £10.22 = £68.62.

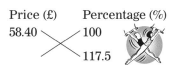

Method 2

Price (£)   Percentage (%)

58.40 ⤬ 100

117.5

Total price including VAT $= \dfrac{58.40 \times 117.5}{100} = £68.62.$

Removing the VAT from the 'VAT-included' price

As you saw in the example above, the 'VAT-included' price is 100% + 17.5% = 117.5% of the original or pre-VAT price.

If you want to find the original price, you need to find the value of 100%, or if you want to find the VAT, you need to find the value of the 17.5%.

Example 1.12

A coffee-maker is priced at £31.49 including VAT. Find its price before VAT was added.

Solution

Price (£)   Percentage (%)

31.49 ⤬ 117.5

100

Pre-VAT price $= \dfrac{31.49 \times 100}{117.5} = 26.8$

The original price was £26.80.

Remember: Not £26.8!

Example 1.13

Find the VAT on a calculator if the price including VAT is £16.92.

Solution

Price (£)   Percentage (%)

16.92 ⤬ 117.5

17.5

VAT $= \dfrac{16.92 \times 17.5}{117.5} = £2.52$

Exercise 1.5

In this exercise, take VAT to be 17.5%.

1 Adam Upp, the book-keeper for the circus, calculates the VAT. If the pre-VAT price of a ticket is £11.50 for adults and £8.50 for children, find the price including VAT.

2 Zena Fobier booked a foreign holiday for £1001.10 including VAT. What would the price be without VAT?

3 Phyl Theeritch paid £426.76 for a coat including VAT. How much VAT did she pay?

Ratio

Ratio is a way in which quantities can be divided.

How much do you know already?

Exercise 1.6

1 Lottie Ree distributed £600 among three people in the ratio 2 : 3 : 7. How much did each receive?

2 Huw Jeego wanted his photo on the circus poster enlarged in all dimensions in the ratio 2 : 5. If the original length is 45 cm, find the new length.

Did you spot X-Direct?

How did you get on?

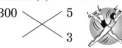

If you managed those questions without any difficulty, you obviously have a method which works for you. However, if you had any problems, see if Ray Showroola and his bed of nails combined with X-Direct, might help.

Meet Ray Showroola

Use this ruler and you'll have ratio nailed!

Ray Showroola in action

Look carefully at these rulers. Count the number of parts in each one. Add up the two numbers in the ratio. Get the idea?

Type 1: The question gives a quantity that relates to the whole of the ruler

Example 1.14

Shirley Knott visited the circus and gave £300 to her two favourite lion tamers, Terry Fyde and Petra Fyde in the ratio of 3 to 2. How much did each receive?

Solution

Write £300 above the whole of the 3 : 2 ratio ruler.

Use X-Direct to find Terry's share.

Share (£)   Sections
300 $\diagdown$ 5
          $\times$
               3

Terry's share = $\dfrac{300 \times 3}{5}$ = £180.

Or work out the money relating to each section.
i.e. £300 ÷ 5 = £60.

Terry receives 3 sections   £60 × 3 = £180

Petra receives 2 sections   £60 × 2 = £120

Check: All the amounts must add up to the original £300.

Example 1.15

Mister Catch, a retired juggler, gave £750 to his successors, Willie, Kenny and Noel Droppitt in the ratio of their years of experience i.e. 7, 6 and 2 respectively. How much did each receive?

Solution

Use X-Direct to find Willie's amount of money.

Share (£)   Sections
750 $\diagdown$ 15
          $\times$
               7

Willie's amount = $\dfrac{750 \times 7}{15}$ = £350

or

Each section represents £750 ÷ 15 = £50.

Willie gets £50 × 7 = £350

Kenny gets £50 × 6 = £300

Noel gets £50 × 2 = £100

Check: 350 + 300 + 100 = 750

Type 2: The quantity given in the question relates to part of the ruler

Example 1.16

Picture frames are made in two sizes. The width of the smaller is 16 cm. The lengths on the larger size are bigger in the ratio 4 : 5. Find the width of the larger frame.

Solution

Start by marking out a ratio ruler with nine divisions, in the ratio 4 : 5.

This time you do not have a total, so do not write anything along the top.

Write the 16 as shown in the diagram.

Now it is a simple matter of using X-Direct to get the answer.

4 : 5

16 :

$$\frac{5 \times 16}{4} = 20$$

Giving ratios in their lowest form

Example 1.17

Give the ratio 2 : 8 : 12 in its lowest form.

Solution

Look for common factors.

(These are numbers which divide into 2, 8 and 12. If you have forgotten about factors, you need to refer to Chapter 2, Number.)

The only common factor of 2, 8 and 12 is 2, so dividing through by this gives 1 : 4 : 6.

Example 1.18

A ratio is given as 5 : 8.

a) Express this ratio in the form $n : 1$.

b) Express this ratio in the form $1 : n$.

Solution

Once again, X-Direct can come to the rescue. Leave a space where the n should come.

a) 5 : 8

   : 1

$$\frac{1 \times 5}{8} = 0.625$$

Answer in the form $n : 1$ is   0.625 : 1

b) 5 : 8

1 :

$$\frac{8 \times 1}{5} = 1.6$$

Answer in the form $1 : n$ is   1 : 1.6

Just to recap

Ray Showroola says:

1   Mark out a ruler showing you all the parts.

2   If you have a total (i.e. the whole amount) which has to be shared, write the amount over the top. You can then see that dividing the total by the number of parts will give you the 'size' of one share. Then it is just a matter of using X-Direct to calculate the other shares.

3   If you do not have the total, but just an increase or decrease in one part, write this underneath the ruler and solve *either* by using X-Direct *or* by working out the size of each section.

Exercise 1.7

1 Share £750 in the ratio 5 : 7 : 13.

2 Money has been shared in the ratio 3 : 2. If the larger amount is £450.00, find the smaller.

3 a) A party from Pause Pelling Grammar School plans to visit the circus. If the ratio of teachers to students must be 2 : 15, how many teachers would be needed to accompany a party of 45 students?

b) If 12 teachers were available, what is the maximum number of students who could accompany them?

Answers

3 a) 6 teachers **b)** 90 students

2 £300

1 £150, £210 and £390

Exercise 1.8

1 Gaye Vaway sells paper plates at 5p each, or in packets of 10 for 40p, or in packets of 50 for £1.85. Find the cheapest way to buy:

a) 9 plates **b)** 20 plates **c)** 110 plates.

2 In a closing down sale, a shop reduces all its prices by 15%. What is the sale price of an item which originally cost £380.00?

3 A gift of £1800 is to be shared among Anne Doubt, Jack Pott and Wynne de Faul in the ratio of their ages: 3, 4 and 2 respectively.

a) How much will each receive?

b) If, instead, the present is deferred for a year, but still divided in the ratio of the ages of the recipients, how much would each receive?

4 A job is advertised as paying an hourly rate of £7.50.

a) How much would be paid for working a 40 hour week?

b) Overtime is paid at a rate of time and a half. How much extra would be paid for six hours overtime?

c) If one week a man earned £401.25, how many hours overtime did he work?

5 The price of an item has been reduced in a sale by 20%. If it now costs £70.00, find its original price.

6 In a college, 80 people were asked what grade they expected to get in Maths. Sadly, 22 of them said that they would be lucky not to get a 'U'. Express this number as a percentage of the whole group asked.

7 A packet contains 24 biscuits. Half of the biscuits are put aside, and the remainder are shared by Ava Garribaldi, Big Di Gestive and Chris Crinkle in the ratio 3 : 4 : 5.

a) What fraction of the original packet does Big Di receive?

b) Chris eats two biscuits. What fraction of his share does he still have?

c) Ava eats one of her biscuits and does not like it, so divides her remaining biscuits equally between Big Di and Chris. What fraction of the original packet has Big Di received altogether?

d) What fraction of the packet of biscuits did Ava eat?

8 The sides of two pictures are in the ratio 5 : 3.

a) If the larger is 35 cm wide, how wide is the smaller?

b) If the smaller is 10.5 cm long, find the length of the larger.

Answers

8 a) 21 cm **b)** 17.5 cm

7 a) $\frac{4}{24} = \frac{1}{6}$ **b)** $\frac{3}{5}$ **c)** $\frac{5}{24}$ **d)** $\frac{1}{24}$

6 27.5% or 28 %

5 £87.50

4 a) £300 **b)** £67.50 **c)** 9 hours

3 b) Anne gets £600, Jack gets £750, Wynne gets £450

3 a) Anne gets £600, Jack gets £800, Wynne gets £400

2 £323.00

1 c) 2 packets of 50 and one packet of 10

b) 2 packets of 10

a) In a packet of 10

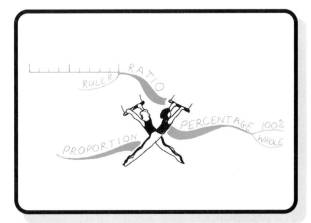

review

How much have you learnt?

Tick off each topic in the list when you are confident you can cope with it.

- Answer questions on direct proportion.

- Answer questions on inverse proportion.

- Find one number as a percentage of another.

- Find a given percentage of a number.

- Increase a price or amount by a given percentage.

- Decrease a price or amount by a given percentage.

- Calculate the percentage discount on a price.

- Calculate the VAT on an article, given the pre-VAT price.

- Calculate the VAT on an article, given the VAT-included price.

- Calculate the VAT-inclusive price of an article, given the pre-VAT price.

- Calculate the pre-VAT price, given the VAT-inclusive price.

- Divide a given number or amount in a given ratio.

- Calculate individual shares of a number or amount divided in a given ratio.

- State ratios in their lowest terms.

- State ratios in the form 1 : *n*.

- State ratios in the form *n* : 1.

- Work out the lengths involved in scale drawing.

2

Number

How much do you know already?

Exercise 2.1

1 Write 23.897 correct to two decimal places (2 d.p.).

2 Write 5468 to two significant figures (2 sig. figs.).

3 Change $\frac{2}{5}$ to **a)** a decimal **b)** a percentage.

4 Use your calculator to work out $\dfrac{16.2 + \sqrt{16.3}}{2.8 + 7.1}$.

  a) Write down all the figures on your calculator display.
  b) Give your answer correct to 3 d.p.
  c) Give your answer correct to 3 sig. figs.
  d) Without using a calculator, give a rough estimate of the answer. Show how you reached your answer.

5 Write the following numbers in standard form.

  a) 5 240 000 000   **b)** 0.000 005 24

6 Evaluate and write the answer in standard form.
$(3.2 \times 10^9) \times (2.1 \times 10^{12})$

7 Evaluate and write the answer in standard form.
$(1.4 \times 10^{15}) \div (6.8 \times 10^8)$

8 Write the following numbers in order of size starting with the smallest.
1.3×10^{12}, 6.2×10^8, 1.7×10^{11}, 8.6×10^9, 7.3×10^8

9 The length of a piece of string is measured to the nearest cm. If the length is given as 12 cm, give its longest and shortest possible measurements.

10 An audience is estimated at 700 to the nearest 100. Give the smallest and largest size it could be.

preview

By the end of this chapter you will be able to:

- round a decimal fraction to a given number of decimal places or significant figures

- round to the nearest 0.5, 1, 10, 50, 100, etc.

- state the limits of rounded numbers

- make estimates of calculations

- write a number as a product of its prime factors

- apply the rules of powers or indices

- express a decimal number in standard form

- compare decimals, fractions and percentages

- answer questions involving rates, such as speed

- express time as a proper decimal

- use formulae to calculate volumes

Using a calculator

Decimal places

Significant figures

Standard form

Estimation

Indices

Distance speed – time –

Product of primes

The Ups and Downs of Numbers

11 Give your answers to the following as a power of 5 where possible.

a) $5^5 \times 5^2$ **b)** $5^5 + 5^2$ **c)** $5^5 \div 5^2$

12 A car travels at 96 km/h. How far does it go in 3 hours 40 minutes?

13 How long would it take the car travelling at this speed to travel 120 km? Give your answer in hours and minutes.

14 Express 840 as a product of its prime factors.

15 $648 = 2^x \times 3^y \times 5^z$

Find x, y and z.

Answers

1 23.90

2 5500

3 a) 0.4   **b)** 40%

4 a) 2.044174328   **b)** 2.044   **c)** 2.04

d) $\dfrac{16+4}{3+7} = \dfrac{20}{10} = 2$

5 a) 5.24×10^9 **b)** 5.24×10^{-6}

6 6.72×10^{21}

7 2.06×10^6

8 6.2×10^8, 7.3×10^8, 8.6×10^9, 1.7×10^{11}, 1.3×10^{12}

9 12.5 cm, 11.5 cm

10 650, 750

11 a) 5^7 **b)** You cannot simplify this as a power of 5.

c) 5^3

12 352 km

13 1 hour 15 minutes

14 $2^3 \times 3 \times 5 \times 7$

15 $x = 3$, $y = 4$, $z = 0$

How did you get on?

All questions right?

Well done! Skim through the rest of the chapter because we have some new methods which might appeal to you.

Less than full marks?

This chapter is not very long, and you shouldn't find it too difficult.

Prime numbers

Prime numbers are whole numbers that have only two factors. The only numbers that divide into a prime number are the number itself and 1.

The first six prime numbers are:

2, 3, 5, 7, 11, 13

Note: 1 is not a prime number. It does not have two factors

The product of primes

This is sometimes called the product of prime factors.

When two numbers are multiplied together, the answer is called the **product**. The two numbers are called **factors**. Factors that are prime numbers are called **prime factors**. Splitting a number into all its prime factors is sometimes referred to as writing the number as the product of its prime factors.

Example 2.1

Write 360 as a product of its prime factors.

This question may also be written in the form '$360 = 2^a \times 3^b \times 5^c$. Find a, b and c.'

Solution

Write down any two factors of 360.

If you have a prime number, ring it.

Split each non-prime number in turn, until all lines end in rings.

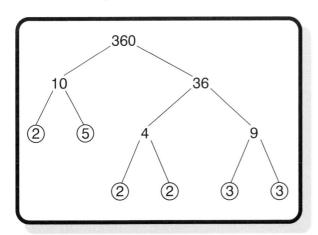

$360 = 2 \times 2 \times 2 \times 3 \times 3 \times 5 = 2^3 \times 3^2 \times 5$

(The answer to the question in the alternative form, above, would be
$a = 3$, $b = 2$ and $c = 1$, since $5 = 5^1$.)

Remember, *any number written to the power of nought (or zero) is 1.*

e.g. $4^0 = 19^0 = 359^0 = 1$

Highest common factor

This is the largest number which divides exactly into two or more numbers. The highest common factor of 12 and 20 is 4. The highest common factor of 50 and 100 is 50.

Exercise 2.2

1 Express 480 as a product of prime factors.

2 Which of the following are prime numbers?
2, 3, 10, 27, 29, 65

3 Find the highest common factor of 60 and 90.

Answers

Approximation

Decimal places

The number of decimal places is the number of digits (figures) that there are in a number, **to the right of the decimal point**.

Example 2.2

Write 4.782 correct to 1 d.p.

Solution

Write the number, and put a ring round the digit which is **one figure to the right** of the required decimal place e.g. 4.7⑧2.

Now decide whether to round up or down by looking at the number which you have ringed. If it is less than 5, you usually round *down*, but if it is 5 or more, you usually round *up*.

4.782 = 4.8 correct to 1 d.p.

Example 2.3

Write 7.304 correct to 2 d.p.

Solution

7.304 = 7.30 correct to 2 d.p.

As the question asks for 2 d.p. you must include the zero.

If the question asks you to give an amount of money to the nearest penny, you are really rounding to two decimal places. If you have to round to the nearest 0.1 cm, you need one decimal place.

Significant figures

The first significant figure is the first digit greater than zero starting from the left.

Example 2.4

Write 28.3762 correct to 3 sig. figs.

Solution

Ring the figure **to the right** of the required number of significant figures. If it is 5 or more, round up; if it is 4 or less round down.

28.3762 = 28.4 to 3 sig. figs.

Example 2.5

Write 7 143 680 correct to 2 sig. figs.

Solution

It may help to notice that large numbers, bigger than 9999, are usually written with spaces before every third number, starting from the right.

7 143 680

The original number is approximately 7 million, so you must be careful to indicate this in your answer by including appropriate zeros. Try writing the original number with a decimal point at the end, and write the approximation directly below.

7 143 680.

7 100 000.

7 143 680 to 2 sig. figs. is 7 100 000.

Remember the noughts. Don't write your answer as 71.

Example 2.6

Write 0.000 759 6 correct to:

a) 1 sig. fig.   **b)** 2 sig. figs.   **c)** 3 sig. figs.

Solution

Note that 7 is the first significant figure as it is the first non-zero digit starting from the left.

a) 0.000 759 6 = 0.0008 to 1 sig. fig.

b) 0.000 759 6 = 0.000 76 to 2 sig. figs.

c) 0.000 759 6 = 0.000 760 to 3 sig. figs.

Remember to include the final zero as it is the third significant figure.

Rounding

Although when using decimal places or significant figures, the above rules apply, you must always read the question carefully. If, for instance, your answer suggests that 5.2 buses are required to carry a certain number of people, you will probably need to round up to 6 to avoid stranded passengers!

If your final answer requires say two decimal places, either use your calculator's memory or else round to four decimal places until the final answer to avoid inaccuracies.

Approximation to the nearest unit

Some questions state that a number has been rounded to the nearest hundred, ten, 0.1 etc. and then ask you to give the highest and lowest possible values that the number could have. The easiest way is to take the hundred, ten etc. and halve it. Then add this half to your original number and subtract half from it.

Example 2.7

The size of an audience was recorded as 650 to the nearest 50. What were the smallest and largest numbers of people that could have been there?

Solution

$50 \div 2 = 25$ Find half of 50.

Smallest value $= 650 - 25$
$= 625$ Take away half of 50.

Largest value $= 650 + 25$
$= 675$ Add on half of 50.

The numbers of people in the audience must have been between 625 and 675.

Example 2.8

A length of 78.6 cm is stated as being correct to the nearest mm. What are its smallest and largest values it could take?

Solution

Think of 1 mm = 0.1 cm.

$0.1 \div 2 = 0.05$

Smallest value

$= 78.6 - 0.05$

$= 78.55$

Largest value

$= 78.6 + 0.05$

$= 78.65$

The value must be between 78.55 cm and 78.65 cm.

Comparing fractions, decimals and percentages

Example 2.9

Write the following in order of size, starting with the smallest.

0.91, 0.905, $\frac{10}{11}$, 90%

Solution

The easiest way is to turn them all into decimals.

$\frac{10}{11} = 10 \div 11 = 0.909\,09\ldots$

$90\% = 90 \div 100 = 0.9$

The order is 90%, 0.905, $\frac{10}{11}$, 0.91.

Indices

In the number 2^3, the 3 is called the **power** or the **index**. (The plural of index is indices.) 2^3 means $2 \times 2 \times 2$, **not** 2×3.

Remember: $2 \times 2 = 2^2 = 4$

Rules of indices

1   *You can only simplify indices when the base number is the same.*

2   *When dividing or multiplying powers of the same number remember TIP and DIM.*

Madam Attix has a card for it.

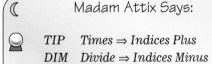

    Madam Attix Says:

   TIP   *Times ⇒ Indices Plus*
   DIM   *Divide ⇒ Indices Minus*

2

Example 2.10

Simplify the following.

a) $3^2 \times 3^5$ **b)** $3^7 \div 3^2$ **c)** $3^2 + 3^5$

d) $4^3 - 4^2$

Solution

a) $3^2 \times 3^5 = 3^7$

b) $3^7 \div 3^2 = 3^5$

c) $3^2 + 3^5$ cannot be simplified as a power of 3.

d) $4^3 - 4^2$ cannot be simplified as a power of 4.

Standard form or standard index form

This is a shorthand method of writing very large or very small numbers. It involves rewriting the number as a number between 1 and 10, multiplied by a power of 10.

Remember:

$10^1 = 10$

$10^2 = 100$

$10^3 = 1000$

$10^8 = 100\,000\,000$

and so on.

Be careful! $10^0 = 1$

Example 2.11

Write $34\,200$ in standard form.

Solution

Rewrite your original number, inserting a decimal point after the first non-zero digit.

3.4200

Note that the decimal point was originally at the right-hand end of the number.

34 200.

3.4200   How many places has the point moved?

Ronnie Mauver the dare-devil rider, moves the decimal point four places in the positive direction.

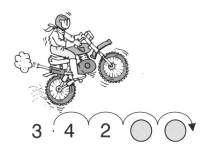

$34\,200 = 3.42 \times 10^4$

The simplest way is to count the number of decimal places you need to return the decimal point to its starting position and write this as a power of 10.

Example 2.12

Write $0.000\,067$ in standard form.

Solution

Ronnie Mauver jumps back five places.

This means that the power will be negative.

Rewriting the original and inserting the required decimal point gives:

000006.7

0.000067

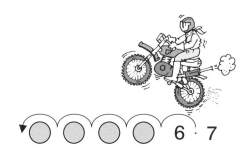

$0.000\,067 = 6.7 \times 10^{-5}$

If your original number is smaller than zero (as it is in this case), write the power of 10 with a negative sign. Remember that if you need to travel back to the start in a negative direction, you need a negative sign.

Most calculators use **EXP** for standard form, but some have a button marked **EE** . Check on your calculator if you are in any doubt.

3.42×10^4 **3** **.** **4** **2** **EXP** **4** **=**

6.7×10^{-5} **6** **.** **7** **EXP** **5** **+/−** **=**

If you can say, 'times 10 to the ...,' replace it with **EXP** or **EE** . **Do not** press

× **1** **0** **EXP** or **×** **1** **0** **EE** .

Exercise 2.3

1 Evaluate $(3.4 \times 10^{22}) \div (1.6 \times 10^9)$. Give your answer in standard form, correct to three significant figures.

2 A book was measured to the nearest centimetre. Its length was given as 30 cm. What was its longest possible length?

3 The speed of light is approximately 2.998×10^8 metres per second. How many metres does it travel in half a minute?

4 a) Mercury is approximately 5.79×10^{10} metres from the sun and Pluto is approximately 5.90×10^{12} metres from the sun. Write the ratio of the distance from the sun of Mercury to Pluto in the form $n : 1$ in standard form, giving your answer correct to three significant figures.

b) Correct to four significant figures, the mass of the Earth is 5.798×10^{24} kg and that of Jupiter is 1.899×10^{27} kg. Write the ratio of the mass of the Earth to that of Jupiter in the form $1 : n$ in standard form, giving your answer correct to four significant figures.

Answers

4 a) $9.81 \times 10^{-3} : 1$ b) $1 : 3.275 \times 10^2$
3 8.994×10^9
2 30.5 cm
1 2.13×10^{13}

TAKE A BREAK

This is a good point to take a short break. The next section is easy, so you shouldn't feel too bad about starting again.

Using your calculator

Examiners often set questions like this.

Evaluate $\dfrac{\sqrt{31.92}}{51.7 - 7.3^2}$

It is important to remember that your calculator will find the square or square root, then multiply or divide, then add or subtract.

Using brackets and sometimes **=** , you can force it to change this order.

Example 2.13

Evaluate $\dfrac{18 + 2}{5}$

Solution

You can see that the answer is $20 \div 5 = 4$ but ...

What would your calculator do? If you keyed in $18 + 2 \div 5$ your calculator would show 18.4, as it would calculate $2 \div 5$ before adding it to 18.

You can avoid this by keying in

1 **8** **+** **2** **=** **÷** **5** **=** or
(**1** **8** **+** **2** **)** **÷** **5** **=**

Either way you get the answer 4, because the 18 and the 2 are added before their sum is divided by 5.

2

Example 2.14

Evaluate $\dfrac{60}{6-1}$

Solution

Key in

| 6 | 0 | ÷ | (| 6 | − | 1 |) | = |

to get the answer 12.

Take care with questions involving square roots,

such as $\dfrac{30}{12-\sqrt{4}}$ for which the answer is 3.

On some calculators, you need to press $\boxed{\sqrt{}}$ $\boxed{4}$, whereas on others you need to reverse this and press $\boxed{4}$ $\boxed{\sqrt{}}$. Experiment with your calculator until you get the right answer.

The following exercise can be solved without using a calculator. We suggest that you work the answers out the long way, then check them on your calculator so that you can be sure you're using it properly.

Remember: *With any calculation, it is a good idea to make an estimate first, so you can check if your answer is sensible.*

Exercise 2.4

Work out the following. Give each answer correct **a)** to 2 decimal places **b)** to 2 significant figures.

1 $\dfrac{5.2 \times 6.3}{2.1 \times 0.7}$

2 $\dfrac{3.6 + 0.2}{8.1 - 0.6}$

3 $\dfrac{2.5^2 - 1.2}{\sqrt{7.4} + \sqrt{0.2}}$

Answers

3 a) 1.59 **b)** 1.6
2 a) 0.51 **b)** 0.51
1 a) 22.29 **b)** 22

Converting time to a decimal number

A common mistake with hours and minutes is to write 2 hours and 45 minutes as 2.45. **This is wrong!**

Remember: There are 60 minutes in an hour.

Think of 45 minutes as $\dfrac{45}{60}$ of an hour.

So 45 minutes = 45 ÷ 60 = 0.75 of an hour (three-quarters of an hour)

and 2 hours 45 minutes is 2.75 hours.

Or use the fraction button!

2 hours 45 minutes

= $\boxed{2}$ $\boxed{a^{b}/_{c}}$ $\boxed{4}$ $\boxed{5}$ $\boxed{a^{b}/_{c}}$ $\boxed{6}$ $\boxed{0}$

If you press $\boxed{=}$, it simplifies the fraction. Then you need to convert this to a decimal. Most calculators will do this if you press the fraction key $\boxed{a^{b}/_{c}}$ again, but on some you need to press the $\boxed{\text{2nd f}}$ or $\boxed{\text{inv}}$ key followed by a different button.

Introducing our famous juggler, Willie Droppitt

And now we invite you to marvel at our latest attraction, the one and only Willie Droppitt, who can help you to juggle formulae. He is here to help you with the next section.

Using formulae

The infallible Willie Droppitt method

To find the value of a letter firstly cover it or cross it out. If the uncovered letters are:

a) on the same level, multiply them

b) on different levels, divide the top one by the bottom one.

Willie Droppitt in action!

Distance, speed, time

$$D = S \times T \qquad S = \frac{D}{T} \qquad T = \frac{D}{S}$$

with D on top, S and T below.

*Remember **D**owning **St**.*

Amount, rate, time

$$A = R \times T \qquad R = \frac{A}{T} \qquad T = \frac{A}{R}$$

with A on top, R and T below.

Remember ART.

Example 2.15

Ella Von Urri drives at 120 km/h. How far does she travel in 3 hours and 25 minutes?

Solution

Firstly, **do not** write 3 hours 25 minutes as 3.25.

3 hours 25 minutes $= 3 + \frac{25}{60}$ or

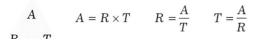

You are asked for the distance.
Cover or cross out D.

S and T are on the same level, so you multiply them.

$$D = S \times T$$
$$= 120 \times 3\tfrac{25}{60}$$
$$= 410 \text{ km}$$

Example 2.16

Hywel Menditt's tap is leaking at a rate of 25 cm³ per second. How long does it take to fill a 1 litre bowl? (1 litre = 1000 cm³)

Solution

$$T = \frac{A}{R}$$
$$= \frac{1000}{25}$$
$$= 40 \text{ seconds}$$

Don't mix units. The rate is in cm³, so change the litre into cm³.

Similarly, if the question involves cm and m, change the metres into centimetres.

Example 2.17

Jenny Da Lifte has to travel 210 kilometres in 3 hours and 30 minutes. Find her average speed in kilometres per hour.

Solution

3 hours 30 minutes = 3.5 hours (not 3.3 hours)

$$S = \frac{D}{T}$$
$$= \frac{210}{3.5}$$
$$= 60 \text{ km/h}$$

Keep this to yourself, but you may find these techniques useful in Physics, too!

Exercise 2.5

In this exercise you have the chance to practise some of the techniques that are covered in chapters 1 and 2. If there is a question that you cannot answer, look back through both chapters for some clues.

1 a) Write a time of 3 hours 24 minutes in decimal form.
 b) Write the decimal form of 5.7 hours in hours and minutes.

2 A teenager plans to spend 40% of each weekday either at school or studying at home.
 a) How many hours a day is this?
 b) Express your answer to **a)** in hours and minutes.
 c) If she counts the school day as lasting 6 hours 30 minutes altogether, how many hours per day does she plan to spend studying at home?
 d) What percentage of the day is spent studying at home, to the nearest 1%?

3 a) A car travels at a speed of 96 km/h. How long does it take to complete a journey of 796.8 km?
 b) Another car completes the same journey in 7 hours 15 minutes. What is its average speed?

4 Water flows out of a leaking tank at the rate of 5.2 litres per second. If the tank originally holds 135 litres, how long would it take for it to empty?

5 a) Without using a calculator, give a rough estimate for 5389×96. Show how you reached your answer.
 b) Without using a calculator, work out the exact answer to 5389×96. You must put down enough working to show that you have not used a calculator.

6 A car travels 18.6 km on 4.4 litres of petrol.
 a) How far does it go on 20 litres?
 b) How many litres would it use to travel 100 km?

7 Write the following numbers in standard form.
 a) 2 380 000 000 000
 b) 0.000 000 007 23
 c) 14 678.3 (Write this answer correct to three significant figures.)

8 Bess Twirk took tests in English, Maths and French. In English she scored $\frac{47}{72}$, in Maths $\frac{38}{60}$ and in French 64%.
 a) Which was her best result?
 b) Which was her worst result?

9 $192 = 2^x \times 3^y \times 5^z$. Find the values of x, y and z.

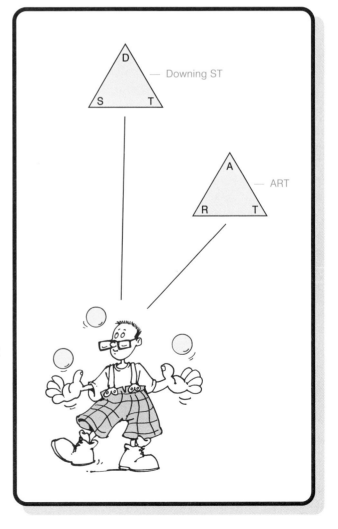

review

How much have you learnt?

Tick off each topic in the list when you are confident you can cope with it.

- Use your calculator properly.
- Round a decimal fraction to a given number of decimal places.
- Round a number to a given number of significant figures.
- Round to the nearest 0.5, 1, 10, 50, 100 etc.
- State the limits of rounded numbers.
- Make estimates of calculations.
- Write a number as a product of its prime factors.
- Apply the rules of powers or indices.
- Express a decimal number in standard form.
- Compare decimals, fractions and percentages.
- Answer questions involving rates, such as speed.
- Express time as a proper decimal.
- Use formulae to calculate volumes.

If you have mastered this chapter and Chapter 1, Proportion, percentages and ratio, it is time for you to tackle the Number review, on page 24.

Number review

1 Use your calculator to evaluate these.

a) $\dfrac{5.76 - 1.42}{6.72 + 2.33}$

b) $\sqrt{(4.72 - 3.17)^2 + 1.76}$

2 Which of the following numbers is the largest?
$\frac{2}{3}, \frac{5}{8}, \frac{7}{11}$

3 Two people score points in the ratio of 7 : 2. If the higher score was 42, what was the lower?

4 Convert 6 feet 2 inches into centimetres.
1 cm ≈ 0.394 inches
12 inches = 1 foot

5 Express $\frac{33}{60}$ as a percentage.

6 A group of 248 people are going on holiday by bus. Each bus costs £310 and can accommodate 52 people. Find the approximate total cost. Do not use a calculator and show all working.

7 When going on holiday, a man converts £620 into 4700 French francs.
a) If his friend changes £590, how many francs will he receive?
b) If they have a total of 1210 francs at the end of the holiday, what would this be worth in pounds?

8 A train travels 288 kilometres in 2 hours 10 minutes. What was its average speed in km/h?

9 Write 0.000 007 02 in standard form.

10 A club of 130 people hires coaches for an event. If each coach can hold 30 people, how many coaches must be hired?

11 The price of a jacket, usually set at £75, is reduced by 15% in a sale. Find the sale price.

Algebra

How much do you know already?

Exercise 3.1

1 Solve for x.
$$7x + 2 = 10x - 13$$

2 Solve for x and y.
$$4x + 3y = 41$$
$$5x - 2y = 34$$

3 Solve this equation for x.
$$x^2 - 17x - 18 = 0$$

4 Rearrange the formula below to make c the subject.
$$t = ad - c^2$$

5 Find the next two numbers in each of the following sequences, and give formulae for the nth term.
a) 2, 5, 8, 11, ...　　　　**b)** 4, 7, 12, 19, ...

preview

By the end of this chapter you will be able to:

- explain the meaning of the words **coefficient, constant** and **variable**

- solve simple linear equations in one unknown

- solve simultaneous equations in two unknowns

- factorise algebraic expressions

- solve quadratic equations by factorising

- find the rule for forming a sequence with equal differences

- find the rule for forming a sequence with unequal differences

- find the nth term of a sequence

- find the value of an unknown in a formula by substitution

- rearrange formulae

- make expressions and equations from statements

6 Given that $a = \dfrac{cm - d}{e - c}$

find a, when $c = -0.7$, $m = 3.4$, $d = -0.15$ and $e = -2$. Give your answer correct to two decimal places.

Answers

1 $x = 5$

2 $x = 8$, $y = 3$

3 $x = 18$, $x = -1$

4 $c = \sqrt{ad - t}$

5 a) 14, 17; nth term $3n - 1$
   b) 28, 39; nth term $n^2 + 3$

6 1.72

How did you get on?

All of them right?
Have you considered taking a Maths degree?

Four or more right?
Why aren't you taking the Higher paper?

Fewer than four right?
The bad news is that this is probably the most difficult chapter in the book. The good news is that our easy methods will make it less difficult and will boost your marks.

Don't let Algebra spook you – our methods are guaranteed ghost busters.

Just to recap

$ab = a \times b$

$\dfrac{a}{b} = a \div b$

$\dfrac{a}{b + c} = a \div (b + c)$

$3a = 3 \times a$

$3a^2 = 3 \times a^2$

$(3a)^2 = 3a \times 3a = 9a^2$

$-a \times -a = a^2$

Evaluating formulae

This type of question is very common. The questions are easy if you can use your calculator properly, but you must be very careful with formulae that involve negative numbers.

Example 3.1

Find z when

$$z = \frac{rs - t}{r + t}$$

and $r = -6.2$, $s = 3.4$ and $t = -5.3$.

Solution

$z = 1.4$

If you did not get this right, you probably either:

a) slipped up with the signs – if you did, learn how to use the +/– key on your calculator, or

b) did not calculate $rs - t$ and $r + t$ before you divided the top by the bottom.

Simple equations

How much do you know already about equations?

Here are some straightforward equations for you to try, just to see how much algebra you have taken in during all those Maths lessons you have sat through over the years.

Exercise 3.2

Evaluate (find the value of) x in the following equations.

1 $x + 2 = 20$

2 $x - 3 = 15.5$

3 $2x + 1 = 15$

4 $5x - 2 = 33$

5 $16 = 24 - 2x$

6 $5x + 20 = 5$

7 $\frac{x}{2} = 10$

8 $\frac{x}{3} + 1 = 5$

9 $5x + 2 = 3x + 18$

10 $2x - 1 = 5x - 28$

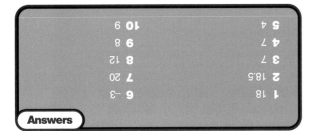

Answers

10 9	**5** 4
9 8	**4** 7
8 12	**3** 7
7 20	**2** 18.5
6 −3	**1** 18

If you managed to get the whole exercise right without our help, you can skip the next section, and turn to 'Simplifying expressions' on page 29. However, if things did not go so well, don't despair, because all the way from Bavaria, to help with solving equations, we are proud to introduce our conjuror, the one and only Hans Zoff.

Meet Hans Zoff
Whatever Hans Zoff does to one side of the equation, he does to the other.

Example 3.2

Find x if $5x + 3 = 23$.

Solution

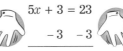

$$5x + 3 = 23$$
$$\underline{\quad -3 \quad -3 \quad}$$ Take 3 from both sides.
$$5x = 20$$
$$\underline{\quad \div 5 \quad \div 5 \quad}$$ Divide both sides by 5.
$$x = 4$$

Check: Put your answer into the original equation to see if your answer is correct.

$$5 \times 4 + 3 = 23$$

Example 3.3 – Using a subtraction sign

Find x if $2x - 15 = 17$.

Solution

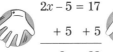

$$2x - 5 = 17$$
$$\underline{\quad +5 \quad +5 \quad}$$ Add 5 to both sides.
$$2x = 22$$
$$\underline{\quad \div 2 \quad \div 2 \quad}$$ Divide both sides by 2
$$x = 11$$ Remember to **check** your answer!

Example 3.4 – With a negative coefficient of x

Solve the equation $4 = 16 - 3x$ to find x.

Solution

$$4 = 16 - 3x$$
$$\underline{\quad +3x \qquad +3x \quad}$$ Add $3x$ to both sides.
$$4 + 3x = 16$$
$$\underline{-4 \qquad\qquad -4 \quad}$$ Subtract 4 from both sides.
$$3x = 12$$
$$x = 4$$ **Check** your answer!

Example 3.5 – Negative answer

Find x if $3x + 10 = 4$.

Solution

$$3x + 10 = 4$$
$$\underline{-10 \quad -10}$$ Subtract 10 from both sides.
$$3x = -6$$
$$\div 3 \quad \div 3$$ Divide both sides by 3.
$$x = -2$$ Because $-6 \div 3 = -2$!
Check your answer!

Example 3.6 – Fractional answer

Find x if $6x - 1 = 2$.

Solution

$$6x - 1 = 2$$
$$\underline{+1 \quad +1}$$ Add 1 to both sides.
$$6x = 3$$
$$\div 6 \quad \div 6$$ Divide both sides by 6 (not $6 \div 3$).
$$x = \tfrac{1}{2}$$ **Check** your answer!

A common error here would be to have an answer of 2. This is one reason why we tell you to check your answer. You should always divide by the **coefficient** of x (which in this case is 6) at this point.

Here are two words to impress your teacher!
A variable is a letter used to stand for an unknown number. In many examples the letter used is x, but you can use any letter.
A coefficient is simply a number in front of a variable. For example, the coefficient of x in 4x is 4, the coefficient of a^2 in $-5a^2$ is -5.

Example 3.7 – Using fractional coefficients

Given that $\dfrac{x}{2} + 1 = 11$, find the value of x.

Solution

$$\frac{x}{2} + 1 = 11$$
$$\underline{-1 \quad -1}$$ Subtract 1 from both sides.
$$\frac{x}{2} = 10$$
$$\times 2 \quad \times 2$$ Multiply both sides by 2.
$$x = 20$$ **Check** your answer!

Balancing act: questions with variables on both sides

In this type of question, you need to take the variables (usually x) on to one side and the rest of the numbers on to the other.

Example 3.8

Find the value of x which satisfies $4x + 7 = 2x + 37$.

Solution

$$4x + 7 = 2x + 37$$
$$\underline{-2x \quad\quad -2x}$$ Take $2x$ from both sides.
$$2x + 7 = 37$$
$$\underline{-7 \quad -7}$$ Subtract 7 from both sides.
$$2x = 30$$
$$\div 2 \quad \div 2$$ Divide both sides by 2.
$$x = 15$$ **Check** your answer!

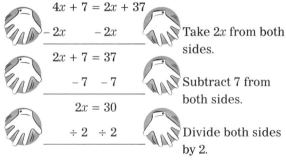

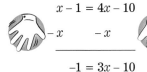

Example 3.9 – With larger coefficient of x on the right

Find the value of x for which $x - 1 = 4x - 10$.

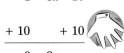Solution

$$x - 1 = 4x - 10$$

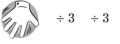 $- x \qquad - x$

You could have subtracted $4x$ from both sides, but this would give a horrible negative coefficient of x.

$$-1 = 3x - 10$$

$+ 10 \qquad + 10$

$$9 = 3x$$

$$3x = 9$$

Swap the equation round.

$\div 3 \quad \div 3$

Divide both sides by 3.

$$x = 3$$

Check your answer!

Now go back and try Exercise 3.2 again. You will almost certainly find it easier this time.

• •

TAKE A BREAK

It's probably time for a break now. This is a long chapter, so don't try to do too much at any one sitting.

• •

Simplifying expressions

Remember: When simplifying expressions, you can only add or subtract like with like. Our pet lions Fee Roshus and Nora Nedoff will demonstrate why.

If a lion is x and a lion tamer is y, then 2 lions and 2 lion tamers can be represented by

$2x + 2y$

Then 2 lions and 2 lion tamers *minus* 1 lion tamer can be represented by

$2x + 2y - y = 2x + y$

Example 3.10

Simplify the following.

a) $x + x$ **b)** $x + x + y + 3$

c) $x^2 + x$ **d)** $x^2 + x^2 + x + 2x$

e) $x^2 + xy + xy + y + 3$

Solution

a) $x + x = 2x$

b) $x + x + y + 3 = 2x + y + 3$

c) $x^2 + x$ cannot be simplified

d) $x^2 + x^2 + x + 2x = 2x^2 + 3x$

e) $x^2 + xy + xy + y + 3 = x^2 + 2xy + y + 3$

How good are you at simplifying expressions?

Exercise 3.3

Simplify the following expressions where possible.

1 $3a + 2a + 5a + b$

2 $10c + 5a - 2a$

3 $2a^2 - a$

4 $6t + 5t^2 - 8t$

5 $5b^2 + 3b - 7b^2$

6 $12x - x^2 - 3x + 10x^2$

Answers

6 $9x^2 + 9x$
5 $3b - 2b^2$
4 $5t^2 - 2t$
3 Cannot be simplified.
2 $10c + 3a$
1 $10a + b$

Expansion of single brackets

Multiply the number outside the bracket with each term inside.

Example 3.11

Expand $3(2x + 5)$.

Solution

$3(2x + 5) = 3 \times 2x + 3 \times 5$

$3(2x + 5) = 6x + 15$

You only need the last line – the others are optional.

Example 3.12

Expand $a(b - c)$.

Solution

$a(b - c) = a \times b + a \times -c$

$a(b - c) = ab - ac$

Remember: The sign is always attached to the number that follows it – which is why we have ringed $-c$.

Example 3.13

Expand $-4(3x + 2y)$.

Solution

$-4(3x + 2y) = -4 \times 3x - 4 \times 2y$

$-4(3x + 2y) = -12x - 8y$

Remember: The minus sign is attached to the 4.

Example 3.14

Simplify $2x(y - 4) - 3(2x - 1)$.

Solution

$$2x(y - 4) - 3(2x - 1) = 2xy - 8x - 6x + 3$$
$$= 2xy - 14x + 3$$

Example 3.15

Simplify $2x - (x - 4)$.

Solution

As there is no number immediately outside the brackets, it is a good idea to put in a 1. That way there is less chance of getting the sign wrong when you expand the brackets.

$$2x - (x - 4) = 2x - 1(x - 4)$$
$$= 2x - x + 4$$
$$= x + 4$$

Remember: $-1 \times -4 = +4$

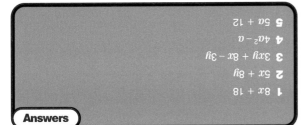

Exercise 3.4

Simplify the following expressions.

1 $3(2x + 4) + 2(x + 3)$

2 $2(x + y) + 3(x + 2y)$

3 $2x(y + 4) + y(x - 3)$

4 $a(2 + a) - 3(a - a^2)$

5 $3(2a + 3) - (a - 3)$

Answers

1 $8x + 18$
2 $5x + 8y$
3 $3xy + 8x - 3y$
4 $4a^2 - a$
5 $5a + 12$

Simple equations with brackets

To find x, expand the brackets, simplify and solve (or evaluate) as we did before.

Example 3.16

Find x where $3(2x - 1) - 4(x - 1) = 15$.

Solution

$$3(2x - 1) - 4(x - 1) = 15$$
$$6x - 3 - 4x + 4 = 15$$
$$2x + 1 = 15$$
$$2x = 14$$
$$x = 7$$

Exercise 3.5

Solve each equation for x.

1 $5(x + 20) = 25$

2 $4(x - 2) = 2(x + 10)$

3 $2 - (x - 3) = -7$

4 $2(x - 1) = 5(x + 2)$

5 $7 - (a - 3) = 3a - 2$

6 $3(x - 4) = 5(x + 3)$

7 $4(x - 2) + 2(x + 5) = 14$

8 $2(x - 1) - 3(x - 2) = 3(x + 5) + 2(3x - 8)$

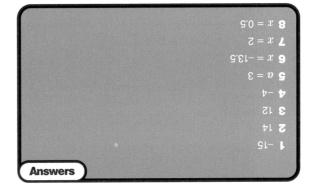

Answers

1 -15
2 14
3 12
4 -4
5 $a = 3$
6 $x = -13.5$
7 $x = 2$
8 $x = 0.5$

Factorising using single brackets

Factorising means splitting a number into its factors. (See Chapter 2, Number if you've forgotten what factors are.) When you factorise you need to find the **highest common factors**, i.e. the biggest numbers or letters that 'go into' all the terms.

Example 3.17

Find the highest common factors of each pair of numbers.

a) 4 and 10

b) 20 and 5

c) a and a^2

d) y^2 and y^3

Solution

a) 2 $4 = 2 \times 2$, $10 = 5 \times 2$

         so the highest common factor, or HCF of 4 and 10 is 2.

b) 5 $20 = 4 \times 5$, $5 = 1 \times 5$

         so the HCF of 20 and 5 is 5.

c) a $a^2 = a \times a$

         so the HCF of a and a^2 is a.

d) y^2 $y^2 = y \times y$ and $y^3 = y \times y \times y$

         so their HCF is $y \times y = y^2$.

Example 3.18

Factorise $10z^2b - 6za$.

Solution

Start with the 10 and the 6.

Their HCF is 2.

Write the 2 outside the brackets.

2( )

If you were simplifying, as you did in the section above, you would have to have 5 and 3 in the brackets in order to multiply out correctly.

$2(5z^2b - 3za)$

Inside the brackets you still have z^2 and z. Their HCF is z, so you can write that outside the brackets as well. As you must be able to multiply out the factorised expression to find the original again, the solution is:

$10z^2b - 6za = 2z(5zb - 3a)$

The letters a and b appear in one term only, so they stay inside the brackets.

Example 3.19

Factorise $6x^2y + 18xy^2$ fully.

Solution

The HCF of 6 and 18 is 6.

$6x^2y + 18xy^2 = 6(x^2y + 3xy^2)$

If it helps, you can cross out the factors as you go along:

$6x^2y + 18xy^2 = 6(x^2y + 3xy^2)$
or
$\not{6}x^2y + \overset{3}{\not{18}}x^2 = 6(x^2y + 3xy^2)$

The HCF of x^2 and x is x.

$6(x^2y + 3xy^2) = 6x(xy + 3y^2)$
or
$6(x\!\!\!/^2y + 3\not{x}y^2) = 6x(xy + 3y^2)$

The HCF of y and y^2 is y.

$6x(xy + 3y^2) = 6xy(x + 3y)$
or
$6x(x\not{y} + 3y\!\!\!/^2) = 6xy(x + 3y)$

So $6x^2y + 18xy^2 = 6xy(x + 3y)$

Check your answer by multiplying out the brackets to make sure that both sides are the same.

Example 3.20

Factorise $12a^2b^2 - 4ab$ fully.

Solution

The HCF of 12 and 4 is 4.

$12a^2b^2 - 4ab = 4(3a^2b^2 - ab)$

or

$\overset{3}{\cancel{12}}a^2b^2 - \overset{}{\cancel{4}}ab = 4(3a^2b^2 - ab)$

The HCF of a^2 and a is a.

$4(3a^2b^2 - ab) = 4a(3ab^2 - b)$

or

$4(3\overset{}{\cancel{a}}^2b^2 - \overset{}{\cancel{a}}b) = 4a(3ab^2 - b)$

The HCF of b^2 and b is b.

So $4a(3ab^2 - b) = 4ab(3ab - 1)$

or

$4a(3ab\overset{}{\cancel{}}^2 - \overset{1}{\cancel{b}}) = 4ab(3ab - 1)$

If all the factors of a term are taken outside the bracket, you have to replace them inside the bracket with a 1, so that when you multiply out the bracket you will get back to your original expression.

Exercise 3.6

Factorise the following expressions.

1 $16ab + 10bc$

2 $4c^2 - 2ac$

3 $10a^2b^2 - 5a$

4 $24x^2y^2 - 12xy$

5 $2a - 10ab$

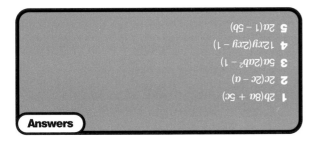

Answers

5 $2a(1 - 5b)$
4 $12xy(2xy - 1)$
3 $5a(2ab^2 - 1)$
2 $2c(2c - a)$
1 $2b(8a + 5c)$

Making expressions and equations from statements

Expressions

Before you look at the solutions of the next example, see if you can work out the expressions by yourself.

Example 3.21

a) Noelle Mett, the stuntsperson, knows that her best friend is eight years younger than she is. If Noelle is x years old, write down an expression for the age of her friend. (**Remember**: If you are asked for an expression, your answer will be in terms of a variable, such as x.)

Solution

a) $x - 8$

b) Lou Kout and Bea Ware are lion tamers. Lou Kout is very experienced – he has survived three weeks – so he is paid three times as much per week as Bea Ware. If Bea Ware earns y pounds per week, find Lou Kout's weekly wage.

Solution

b) $3y$

c) Paul E. Payde earns £5 per hour for his Saturday job.
  i) If he works n hours, how much does he get paid?
  ii) If he also gets £10 in tips, how much money will he take home?

Solution

c) i) $5n$ **ii)** $5n + 10$

Example 3.22

Eva Rupp is too heavy for acrobatics. She now weighs twice as much as her friend Honor Dyatt, who weighs x kg.

a) Write an expression for Eva's weight.

b) Write an expression for their combined weight.

Simplify your expression.

c) If their combined weight is 138 kg, write an equation in x and solve it to find the weight of each of them.

Solution

Gaynor Mark's dictionary states that whenever you can write 'is' or 'are' in a sentence, you can replace the word by '='. In plain everyday English, it would make sense to say, 'Eva is twice as heavy as' instead of, 'Eva weighs twice as much as', so Eva's weight = 2 × Honor's weight.

a) As Honor's weight is x kg, Eva's = $2x$.

b) Their combined weight = $x + 2x = 3x$.

c) $3x = 138$ kg

$x = 46$ kg so $2x = 92$ kg

Honor Dyatt weighs 46 kg, Eva Rupp weighs 92 kg.

Some questions may ask you for mass instead of weight. Don't be put off. The method is the same.

Exercise 3.7

1 Serge O'Hedd and Liza Round took a test. Serge O'Hedd scored ten marks more than Liza.
   a) If Liza's mark was y, find in terms of y:
      i) Serge's mark   **ii)** their total mark.
   b) If their total score was 65, write an equation in y and solve this to find their individual marks.

2 Vic Taurius and Bjorn Looza had several goes on the hoopla stall. Vic won three times as many prizes as Bjorn.
   a) If Bjorn Looza won n prizes, write an expression for the number won by Vic Taurius.
   b) Write an expression for the total number of prizes won.
   c) If, between them, they collected 68 prizes, how many prizes did Vic receive?

3 Besides being too heavy, Eva Rupp is now too old for the high wire. She is 20 years older than the current star, Honor Dyatt. Take Eva's age as x years.
   a) Write an expression in x for Honor Dyatt's age.
   b) In terms of x, how old will each be in two years' time?
   c) In two years' time Eva will be twice as old as Honor. Write this statement as an equation, and solve it to find their current ages.

4 Wanda Lust and her friend Sandie Beech are saving up to go on holiday. They find that Sandie has £30.00 less than Wanda. After six months of really saving hard, each has managed to save an extra £20.00. Take the amount that Wanda starts with as £x.
   a) Write an expression for the amount of money in pounds that Sandie has at the start.
   b) Write an expression for the amount of money in pounds that Wanda has after six months.
   c) Write an expression for the amount of money in pounds that Sandie has after six months.
   d) After six months Wanda has twice as much money as Sandie. Write this as an equation and solve it.

Answers

1 a) i) $y + 10$ **ii)** $2y + 10$
   b) $2y + 10 = 65$, $2y = 55$, $y = 27.5$, so Serge scored 37.5, Liza scored 27.5.
2 a) $3n$ **b)** $4n$ **c)** $4n = 68$, $n = 17$, Vic won 51 prizes.
3 a) $x - 20$ **b)** $x + 2$, $x - 18$
   c) $x + 2 = 2(x - 18)$, ages 18 and 38
4 a) $x - 30$ **b)** $x + 20$
   c) $x - 10$ because $x - 30 + 20 = x - 10$
   $x + 20 = 2(x - 10)$ so $x = 40$

TAKE A BREAK

Time for another rest before you tackle Simultaneous equations.

Simultaneous equations

Simultaneous equations are two equations involving two variables (usually x and y), and you are asked to find the values of x and y which satisfy both equations at once, or simultaneously.

> Madam Attix Says:
>
> Simultaneous equations are **SEXY** because for Simultaneous Equations you need to find x and y.

There are several ways of solving simultaneous equations by algebra, but don't worry, we'll only show you one in this chapter.

Elimination

This is the most common method, and one that always works as long as you make sure all the variables are on the same side of the equations. If, for instance, you have $4x = 22 - 2y$, you must first rearrange it to get $4x + 2y = 22$.

Example 3.23 – The coefficients of either x or y are the same

Solve the following simultaneous equations.

$4x + 2y = 22$

$3x + 2y = 19$

Solution

Remember:

1 *You must have the same coefficient in both equations for one of the letters (ignoring whether it is positive or negative). In our example there is a 2y in each of the equations.*

2 *If the signs of these are the same, you take away one equation from the other, and if the signs are opposite you add (plus) them.*

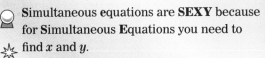

> Madam Attix Says:
>
> **STOP** – **S**ame **T**ake, **O**pposite **P**lus.

3 *In our example, both 2ys are positive (same sign and 'same take, opposite plus'), so we must take away.*

Box the terms that will cancel out.

$4x + \boxed{2y} = 22$
$3x + \boxed{2y} = 19$
_____
$\qquad x = 3$

$(4x - 3x = x,\ 22 - 19 = 3)$

Remember: *Simultaneous equations are sexy – you need to find both x and y.*

Use the easier equation.

$3x + 2y = 19$
$\ 9 + 2y = 19 \quad$ because $3x = 3 \times 3 = 9$
$\quad\ \ 2y = 10$
$\qquad y = 5$

Check: Use the other equation ($4x + 2y = 22$).

$4 \times 3 + 2 \times 5 = 22$

The answer is $x = 3$, $y = 5$.

Example 3.24

Find the values of x and y which satisfy these equations.

$3x + 2y = 16$

$\ x + y\ = 5$

Solution

$3x + 2y = 16 \qquad$ **1**

$\ x + y\ = 5 \qquad$ **2**

Ignoring the signs, are the coefficients of either variable (letter) the same? No.

It is usually easier to multiply the equation with the lower coefficient to make the coefficients of either x or y the same (ignoring signs). As we have chosen to eliminate y, we have multiplied the second equation by 2. (If instead you chose to eliminate x, you would have to multiply the equation by 3.)

Remember: You need to multiply the whole equation.
If $x + y = 5$ then $2x + 2y = 10$.

$$3x + 2y = 16 \qquad \mathbf{1}$$
$$2x + 2y = 10 \qquad \mathbf{2} \times 2$$
$$\overline{\qquad x = 6 \qquad}$$

The signs of the ys are the same, so we've taken one equation from the other.   **STOP**

Having found x we need to find y, so substitute x back into the easier of the two original equations.   **SEXY**

$$x + y = 5$$
$$6 + y = 5$$
$$y = -1$$

Check in equation **1**: $3 \times 6 + 2 \times -1 = 16$

This is true so your answers for x and y are true.

Exercise 3.8

Find x and y in the following equations.

1 $x + 8y = 17$
   $x + y = 10$

2 $5x + 2y = 26$
   $3x + 2y = 18$

3 $6x + 5y = 67$
   $6x + 3y = 45$

Example 3.25

Solve these equations.

$5x - 4y = 32$

$3x + 4y = 0$

Solution

Ignoring the signs, the coefficients of y are the same.

The signs are opposite for the $4y$s so the equations must be added.

$$5x - 4y = 32$$
$$3x + 4y = 0$$
$$\overline{\qquad 8x = 32}$$
$$\qquad x = 4$$

STOP: 'same take, opposite plus'

Having found x you must find y.

Remember: Simultaneous equations are sexy!

Using the simpler second equation, $3x + 4y = 0$

$12 + 4y = 0$
$$4y = -12$$
$$y = -3$$

Check your answers by substituting them into the original formulae.

Just to recap

1   Make the coefficients for either the x or y terms the same, ignoring signs. Multiply if necessary.

2   Use STOP to find either x or y.

3   Remember SEXY and find the other value.

4   **Check**.

Exercise 3.9

Find x and y in the following equations.

1 $x + 5y = 35$
$2x + 3y = 14$

2 $7x - 2y = 110$
$x + 2y = 50$

3 $5x + 4y = 47$
$2x + 3y = 23$

4 $3x + 4y = 65$
$2x + 5y = 76$

5 On Tuesday, Anna Bollick lifted five small weights and four large weights, totalling 175 kg. Her great rival, Clem Bewteroll, lifted 178 kg in the form of eight small weights and three large weights. Taking the weight, in kg, of a small weight as x and of a large as y, form two equations in x and y, and solve them to find the weight of:
a) a small weight   **b)** a large weight.

6 Andy Chapterno, the Italian odd job man, helps to assemble the Big Top using short and long rods that are x and y metres long respectively. The tallest pole which he must assemble is 22.5 m and is made up of four short and six long rods. The shortest pole uses five short and four long rods and is 18.5 m. Use this information to find the length of short and long rods.

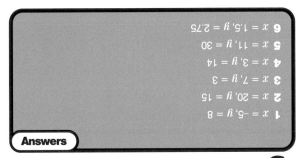

Answers

1 $x = -5$, $y = 8$
2 $x = 20$, $y = 15$
3 $x = 7$, $y = 3$
4 $x = 3$, $y = 14$
5 $x = 11$, $y = 30$
6 $x = 1.5$, $y = 2.75$

Remember: *You can solve simultaneous equations graphically by finding the point where two lines cross. You can find out more about that on page 59.*

TAKE A BREAK

Time for tea? Take a break before tackling quadratics.

Multiplying out (expanding) double brackets

We are using FOIL (**F**irst **O**uter **I**nner **L**ast) to expand double brackets. If you've learnt another method, feel free to use it.

Example 3.26

Expand $(x + 1)(2x + 3)$.

Solution

Using FOIL   First   Outer   Inner   Last

$(x + 1)(2x + 3) = x \times 2x + x \times 3 + 1 \times 2x + 1 \times 3$
$= 2x^2 + 3x + 2x + 3$
$= 2x^2 + 5x + 3$

A common mistake is to add the last terms instead of multiplying them.

You can leave out the first line of working – we included it just to show how we got the terms.

Factorising using double brackets

In this section we shall show you how to rewrite a quadratic expression (i.e. one containing an x^2), putting it into two brackets. As you have just spent the last section making a quadratic expression out of two brackets, this may seem a rather curious activity, but the exam may test either skill, and a few more marks are always worth having!

There are, as usual, several approaches. Try the exercise that follows, and if you can do it go on to the section on 'Rearranging formulae' on page 43.

Exercise 3.10

Factorise the following expressions.

1 $x^2 + 6x + 8$

2 $x^2 + 9x + 20$

3 $x^2 - 9x + 20$

4 $x^2 + 11x - 12$

5 $x^2 - 7x - 30$

Answers

5 $(x - 10)(x + 3)$

4 $(x + 12)(x - 1)$

3 $(x - 5)(x - 4)$

2 $(x + 5)(x + 4)$

1 $(x + 4)(x + 2)$

How to factorise

When you multiply out double brackets, you usually finish up with three terms – an x^2 term, an x term and a term without x, sometimes called a **constant**, e.g. $(x + 3)(x + 2) = x^2 + 5x + 6$.

This is another word you can use to impress your teacher!

Factorising is the reverse of FOIL.

1 The x^2 term is usually made by putting an x in the first place in each bracket. At Intermediate level there should not be any coefficient in front of the x, so you can immediately write down two brackets like this.

$(x \quad)(x \quad)$

2 The other two numbers will involve the factors of the constant. Split the constant into pairs of factors. For the expression $x^2 + 5x + 6$, the constant is 6. The pairs of factors are:

1   2

6   3

3 Separating the terms will be two signs. These could be two positives, two negatives, or one of each.

$(x + ?)(x + ?)$ $(x - ?)(x - ?)$

$(x + ?)(x - ?)$ $(x - ?)(x + ?)$

To decide which type you have, firstly look at the *second sign* in the original equation.

$x^2 + ?x + ?$ $x^2 - ?x - ?$

$x^2 + ?x - ?$ $x^2 - ?x + ?$

In the example $x^2 + 5x + 6$, the second sign is positive.

Type 1: The second sign in the expression is positive

If the second sign is positive, both signs in the brackets will be the same. (*Plus* and *same* both have four letters.)

If the first sign is positive, both signs in the brackets are positive.

If the first sign is negative, both signs in the brackets are negative.

Now go back to the pairs of factors which you wrote down and put positive or negative signs in front of each number, according to which sign you are going to need.

$x^2 + 5x + 6$

Since the first sign is positive:

+1   +2

+6   +3

One pair of factors when added must total the coefficient of x, in this case 5.

When you add up the columns, you can see that only $2 + 3$ gives the required total 5, so the answer is

$x^2 + 5x + 6 = (x + 3)(x + 2)$

Check your answer using FOIL.

Example 3.27

Factorise $x^2 + 12x + 20$.

Solution

The pairs of factors making up 20 are:

1	2	4
20	10	5

The second sign is + (positive), so both signs are the same.

The first sign is +, so both signs will be +.

Inserting the +s and totalling the pairs gives:

+1	+2	+4
+20	+10	+5
21	12	9

As the original expression has $12x$, the answer is:

$x^2 + 12x + 20 = (x + 10)(x + 2)$

Exercise 3.11

Factorise the following expressions.

1 $x^2 + 11x + 10$

2 $x^2 - 6x + 8$

3 $x^2 - 13x + 36$

4 $x^2 + 11x + 24$

Answers

4 $(x + 8)(x + 3)$
3 $(x - 9)(x - 4)$
2 $(x - 4)(x - 2)$
1 $(x + 10)(x + 1)$

Type 2: The second sign in the expression is negative

If the second sign is negative, both signs in the brackets will be different. (*Different* and *minus* both have i as their second letter.)

Example 3.28

Factorise $x^2 - 9x + 20$.

Solution

List the factors of 20.

1	2	4
20	10	5

The second sign is positive, so both signs are the same.

The first sign is negative, so both signs will be negative.

−1	− 2	−4
−20	−10	−5
−21	−12	−9

$x^2 - 9x + 20 = (x - 5)(x - 4)$

Example 3.29

Factorise $x^2 + 11x - 12$.

Solution

List the factors of 12.

1	2	3
12	6	4

The second sign is negative, so the signs will be different.

To decide which way round to put the factors, look at the first sign in the expression.

If it is positive, this means that the larger factor is positive.

If it is negative, this means that the larger factor is negative.

39

As 11 is positive, put + in front of the larger number in each pair of factors, and – in front of the smaller. Then total them in the usual way.

–1	–2	–3
+12	+6	+4
11	4	1

$x^2 + 11x - 12 = (x + 12)(x - 1)$

Example 3.30

Factorise $x^2 - 7x - 30$.

Solution

List the factors of 30.

1	2	3	5
30	15	10	6

The second sign is negative, so the signs in the brackets will be different.

The first sign is –, so the larger factor is negative.

1	2	3	5
–30	– 15	–10	– 6
–29	–13	–7	–1

$x^2 - 7x - 30 = (x - 10)(x + 3)$

Just to recap

1 Look at the sign of the constant term (the *second* sign).

   plus ⇒ same sign

   minus ⇒ different signs

2 List the pairs of factors.

3 By looking at the x term, give the factors the appropriate signs.

4 Complete the brackets.

Exercise 3.12

Factorise each of these expressions.

1 $x^2 + 8x - 9$

2 $x^2 + 7x - 18$

3 $x^2 - 3x - 28$

4 $x^2 - 24x - 25$

Answers

4 $(x - 25)(x + 1)$
3 $(x - 7)(x + 4)$
2 $(x + 9)(x - 2)$
1 $(x + 9)(x - 1)$

Unfortunately, examiners won't tell you whether you have a Type 1 or Type 2 expression. However, if you always start by looking at the second sign and then following the above procedure, you should be able to cope with anything they might throw at you.

Here are some mixed examples for you to try.

Exercise 3.13

Factorize these expressions.

1 $x^2 + 14x + 45$

2 $x^2 + 5x - 6$

3 $x^2 - 11x + 24$

4 $x^2 - x - 12$

Answers

4 $(x - 4)(x + 3)$
3 $(x - 3)(x - 8)$
2 $(x + 6)(x - 1)$
1 $(x + 9)(x + 5)$

The bare bones of factorisation

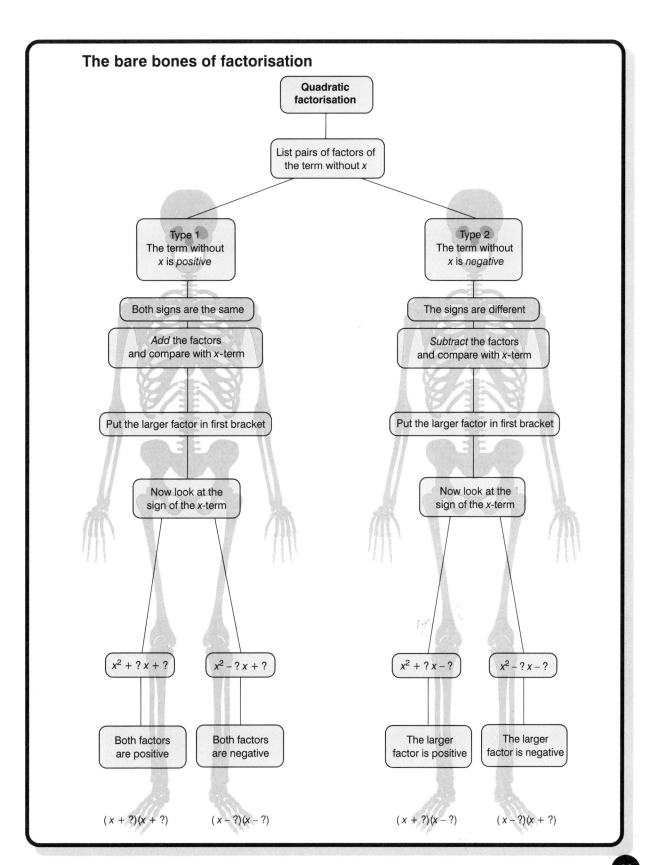

Quadratic factorisation

List pairs of factors of the term without x

Type 1
The term without x is *positive*

Both signs are the same

Add the factors and compare with x-term

Put the larger factor in first bracket

Now look at the sign of the x-term

$x^2 + ?x + ?$

$x^2 - ?x + ?$

Both factors are positive

Both factors are negative

$(x + ?)(x + ?)$

$(x - ?)(x - ?)$

Type 2
The term without x is *negative*

The signs are different

Subtract the factors and compare with x-term

Put the larger factor in first bracket

Now look at the sign of the x-term

$x^2 + ?x - ?$

$x^2 - ?x - ?$

The larger factor is positive

The larger factor is negative

$(x + ?)(x - ?)$

$(x - ?)(x + ?)$

Solving quadratic equations

If you can factorise quadratic expressions, quadratic equations are a piece of cake!

You just need to make sure you have an equation with 0 on one side and a quadratic expression on the other.

Example 3.31

Solve $x^2 + 11x + 10 = 0$.

Solution

Factorise the equation:

$(x + 10)(x + 1) = 0$

Whenever two numbers are multiplied together and the answer is zero, one or the other must be zero.

$(x + 10)$ and $(x + 1)$ represent these two numbers which are multiplied together to make zero.

Therefore, either $(x + 10) = 0$ or $(x + 1) = 0$.

If $x + 10 = 0$, $x = -10$.

If $x + 1 = 0$, $x = -1$.

Example 3.32

Solve $x^2 - 9x - 22 = 0$.

Solution

Factorising the equation gives:

$(x - 11)(x + 2) = 0$

Therefore $(x - 11) = 0$, or $(x + 2) = 0$.

Therefore $x = 11$, or $x = -2$.

Exercise 3.14

Here are the expressions from Exercise 3.12 rewritten as quadratic equations. Solve them to find the values of x.

1 $x^2 + 8x - 9 = 0$

2 $x^2 + 7x - 18 = 0$

3 $x^2 - 3x - 28 = 0$

4 $x^2 - 24x - 25 = 0$

Now you're off to a flying start, try these.

5 $x^2 - 3x - 10 = 0$

6 $x^2 + 8 = 9x$

7 $x^2 + 6x = 7$

Hint: Remember to rearrange **6** and **7** before you try to factorise.

7 $(x + 7)(x - 1) = 0$, so $x = -7$ or $x = 1$
6 $(x - 8)(x - 1) = 0$, so $x = 8$ or $x = 1$
5 $(x - 5)(x + 2) = 0$, so $x = 5$ or $x = -2$
4 $(x - 25)(x + 1) = 0$, so $x = 25$ or $x = -1$
3 $(x - 7)(x + 4) = 0$, so $x = 7$ or $x = -4$
2 $(x + 9)(x - 2) = 0$, so $x = -9$ or $x = 2$
$x = -9$, or $x = 1$
1 $(x + 9)(x - 1) = 0$, so $x = -9$, or $x - 1 = 0$;

Answers

Don't worry if, like many students, you find factorising hard. With practice it gets easier and you will gradually get used to the most commonly occurring pairs of factors.

TAKE A BREAK

Are you still with us? If so, you can celebrate by taking a few minutes off.

Rearranging formulae

Many students think that rearranging formulae (or formulas, you will find both words used) is going to be difficult. However, if you can solve simple equations like the examples at the beginning of the chapter, you shouldn't have any problems. In fact, if you have survived this far into this algebra chapter, you have learned more than enough techniques to solve any of the formula questions which the examiners might dream up.

How much do you know already?

Exercise 3.15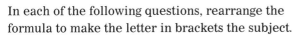

In each of the following questions, rearrange the formula to make the letter in brackets the subject.

1 $a = b + c$ (b)

2 $d = e - f$ (e)

3 $a = x - y$ (y)

4 $ab = z$ (b)

5 $\dfrac{a}{x} = z$ (a)

6 $\dfrac{s}{t} = p$ (t)

7 $b = ac + d$ (a)

8 $y(x - z) = s$ (x)

9 $t = b - ak$ (k)

10 $v = h^2 + t$ (h)

11 $s = c + \sqrt{b}$ (b)

12 $e = b - \sqrt{c}$ (c)

13 $b = \dfrac{c}{e - f}$ (e)

14 $c = 2\pi r$ (r)

Answers

1 $b = a - c$

2 $e = d + f$

3 $y = x - a$

4 $b = \dfrac{z}{a}$

5 $a = xz$

6 $t = \dfrac{s}{p}$

7 $a = \dfrac{b - d}{c}$

8 $x = z + \dfrac{s}{y}$

9 $k = \dfrac{b - t}{a}$

10 $h = \sqrt{v - t}$

11 $b = (s - c)^2$

12 $c = (b - e)^2$

13 $e = \dfrac{c}{b} + f$

14 $r = \dfrac{c}{2\pi}$

How did you get on?

All, or most of them right?

Well done! You should be able to cope with any formula rearrangement question which appears on an Intermediate paper.

The first nine right, but the last few defeated you?

Your only problem is one of confidence. You solved the first nine formulae, didn't you? Well then, you have shown that you can think logically, and that is all you need to do to solve the more involved examples. As you get to grips with the routines that we're about to demonstrate, you will soon begin to wonder why you ever had any problems with formula rearrangement.

The first six right but the rest wrong?

You have the basic ideas well established, but you just need more practice in combining the processes.

Don't even ask?

If it's any comfort, most Intermediate level students (and a good many Higher level students too), start off in much the same position as you are now. However, almost everyone can rearrange formulae, given a little help from the next characters to be introduced.

Rearranging formulae with Simon Nova and Susannah Porter

To their friends they are known as Su and Cy (pronounced 'sigh').

Cy Nova and Su Porter work the human cannon ball.

Su Porter supports the letter which is to become the new subject of the formula, whilst Cy Nova shoots all the surplus letters and numbers over the = sign, changing their sign as he does so.

+ and − change with each other.

× and ÷ change with each other.

Of course, they don't *actually* do anything of the kind. Formulae behave just like any other equations, and you are really adding, subtracting, multiplying or dividing both sides of an equation, as shown on pages 26 – 29. However, you may find it easier to imagine Cy Nova firing symbols or numbers across the = sign, changing the sign as he does so.

Example 3.33

Rearrange this formula, making b the subject.

$$a = b + c$$

Solution

Su Porter supports the b.

Cy Nova fires the c across the =, changing it to $-c$.

$$a - c = b$$

$$b = a - c$$

It is usually a good idea to leave the term you want alone until the end, and start by getting rid of all the surplus letters and terms which are on the same side of the equation.

Example 3.34

Make e the subject of this formula.

$$d = e - f$$

Solution

Su Porter supports the e, whilst Cy Nova shoots the f over to the opposite side, changing its sign as he does so.

$$d + f = e$$

$$e = d + f$$

Example 3.35

Make y the subject of this formula.

$a = x - y$

Solution

Su Porter is not happy holding negative terms, so Cy Nova shoots the y over the $=$ sign to make it positive.

This is not absolutely essential at this stage, but it does make the later operations much easier.

$a + y = x$

Now Su Porter can support the y whilst Cy Nova shoots the a across to give:

$y = x - a$

Example 3.36

Make b the subject of this formula.

$ab = z$

Solution

Su Porter supports the term containing the required letter. As there are no other terms in the equation, Cy Nova can shoot the a across.

As you already know, ab is the algebraic way of writing $a \times b$, so he turns the new expression into a division sum.

The answer is:

$b = \dfrac{z}{a}$

A common mistake is to write $b = \dfrac{a}{z}$.

You can avoid this by first writing down anything which hasn't been moved.

The z has remained in the same place, so start by writing $b = z$.

As the a is moving, it is a that changes sign (from $\times$ to $\div$), and not z.

Example 3.37

Make a the subject of this formula.

$\dfrac{a}{x} = z$

Solution

This is much easier than it might first appear! Su Porter supports the a, so all Cy Nova has to do is to shoot the x up to join the z.

To 'undo' dividing by x, just multiply by x.

$a = zx$

If the required letter is on the bottom, you have to get it to the top as soon as possible.

Example 3.38

Make t the subject of this formula.

$\dfrac{s}{t} = p$

Solution

Su Porter does not like the t in the denominator of the fraction.

Cy Nova shoots the t across to give:

$s = tp$

Then he shoots the p down to the other side and the expression becomes:

$\dfrac{s}{p} = t$

or $t = \dfrac{s}{p}$

Short cut

Can you see that t and p have changed places? This is easier to understand if you use numbers.

$\dfrac{20}{10} = 2$ so $\dfrac{20}{2} = 10$

If you don't want to use this short cut you don't have to. Just continue using Su and Cy in the usual way.

Example 3.39

Make a the subject of this formula.

$b = ac + d$

Solution

Su Porter supports the ac, whilst Cy Nova shoots over the d.

$b - d = ac$

Then he shoots over the c to give:

$\dfrac{b - d}{c} = a$

Example 3.40

Make k the subject of this formula.

$t = b - ak$

Solution

Su Porter holds the ak. As it includes the subject and it is negative, it is a good idea to make it positive at the outset.

Shoot it over to get:

$t + ak = b$

Then you can shoot over the t to get:

$ak = b - t$

As you need the k by itself, shoot across the a to leave:

$k = \dfrac{b - t}{a}$

Example 3.41

Make h the subject of this formula.

$v = h^2 + t$

Solution

Start in exactly the same way as before.

$v - t = h^2$

To 'undo' a squared number, you find its square root, so taking the square root of both sides, gives:

$\sqrt{v - t} = h$

Example 3.42

Make b the subject of this formula.

$s = c + \sqrt{b}$

Solution

Start in exactly the same way.

$s - c = \sqrt{b}$

To 'undo' the square root, you have to square both sides. As the term on the left-hand side is $s - c$, you get:

$(s - c)^2 = b$

Note: You do not get $s^2 - c^2 = b$.

Example 3.43

Make c the subject of this formula.

$e = b - \sqrt{c}$

Solution

As you have a negative subject, start by shooting it over into a positive value.

$e + \sqrt{c} = b$

Then you have to shoot the e over.

$\sqrt{c} = b - e$

Finally, squaring both sides gives:

$c = (b - e)^2$

Example 3.44

Make e the subject of this formula.

$$b = \frac{c}{e} - f$$

Solution

Start in the usual way by shooting over the f.

$$b + f = \frac{c}{e}$$

Now, because the required subject is on the bottom, i.e. dividing, you must bring it to the top.

$$e(b + f) = c$$

Because you need e by itself, $(b + f)$ must be shot to the other side to give:

$$e = \frac{c}{b + f}$$

Example 3.45

Make r the subject of this formula.

$$V = \frac{4}{3}\pi r^3$$

Solution

This is about the most complicated example which you might get, but you have already practised all the necessary skills, so it shouldn't prove to be too much of a problem.

You may find it easier to rewrite the expression as:

$$V = \frac{4}{3}\pi r^3 = \frac{4\pi r^3}{3}$$

Start by bringing the 3 across to the top.

$$3V = 4\pi r^3$$

Then divide by 4π.

$$\frac{3V}{4\pi} = r^3$$

Just as you 'undo' a square number by finding the square root, you 'undo' a cube by finding the cube root.

$$\sqrt[3]{\frac{3V}{4\pi}} = r$$

It is worth persevering with this example, since it occurs quite often on exam papers.

How much have you learnt?

Exercise 3.16

In the following examples, rearrange the formula to make the letter in the bracket the subject.

1 $d = ab - r$ (r)

2 $A = \pi r^2$ (r)

3 $aw^2 = v$ (a)

4 $C = 20h + t$ (t)

5 $C = 20h + t$ (h)

6 $c^3 - a = b$ (c)

7 $ah - t = w$ (t)

8 $y - xw = t$ (x)

Answers

4 $t = C - 20h$

3 $a = \dfrac{v}{w^2}$

2 $r = \sqrt{\dfrac{A}{\pi}}$

1 $r = ab - d$

8 $x = \dfrac{t - y}{n}$

7 $t = ah - w$

6 $c = \sqrt[3]{a + b}$

5 $h = \dfrac{C - t}{20}$

TAKE A BREAK

Even we have to admit it – that was difficult! This time, you can comfort yourself with a short rest and the knowledge that it's downhill from here on.

3

Sequences

Meet DINO and COSTAS

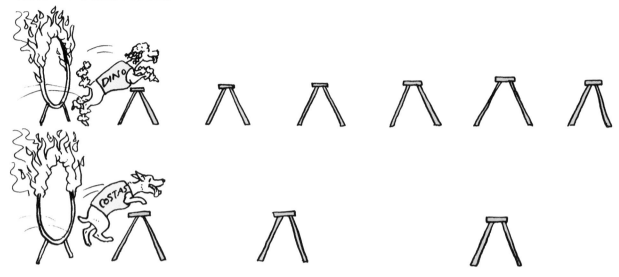

Now we introduce Ringo's performing dogs, DINO and COSTAS, with their revolutionary ways of solving sequences.

DINO likes things laid out with equal spacing, whereas COSTAS likes the differences to get larger.

Sequences with equal spacing

Example 3.46

The following numbers form a sequence.

9, 16, 23, 30, ...

a) What is the difference between consecutive terms?

b) What is the next term in the sequence?

c) What is the nth term?

d) What is the 25th term?

Solution

a) 9, 16, 23, 30, ...

The difference between consecutive terms is 7.

b) The next term is given by 30 + 7 = 37.

c) Here we can use DINO, as the numbers are evenly spaced apart with a difference of 7. Put a ring before the first term.

$\bigcirc$, 9, 16, 23, 30, ...

What number would go in here if there were a number before the 9?

Answer: 9 – 7 = 2

2, 9, 16, 23, 30, ...

DI stands for the difference (7), N stands for n and O stands for the number in the ring (2).

DINO gives $7n + 2$.

Check: If you put $n = 1$, you should get the first term, $7 \times 1 + 2 = 9$.
$n = 2$ gives the second term, 16, etc.

d) To find the 25th term, put $n = 25$, which gives $7 \times 25 + 2 = 177$

Once you get used to using DINO it is fast, failsafe and fun.

Example 3.47

The following numbers form a sequence.

1, 8, 15, 22, 29, ...

a) Find an expression for the nth term.

b) If the kth term is 120, find the value of k.

Solution

a) Using DINO, DI =7, O = –6

So the nth term is $7n - 6$

b) The kth term is 120. It is also $7k - 6$.

So $7k - 6 = 120$, therefore $k = 18$.

Sequences with unequal spacing

Example 3.48

a) What is the next term in this sequence?

3, 6, 11, 18, ...

b) What is the nth term in the sequence?

Solution

a) Look at the differences between the terms. You can see that the difference increases by 2 every term, so the next difference must be 9. The next term must be $18 + 9 = 27$.

b) The differences are not equal so try COSTAS (Cube Or Square, Times, Add, Subtract).

Write the sequence down, with the number of each term above it. First try squaring the n (as squaring is easier than cubing), and comparing to see if you can see a link between the squared numbers and each term. (If you cannot, try cubing them.)

n	1	2	3	4
n^2	1	4	9	16
	3	6	11	18

Now you can see that you have to add 2 to n^2 to get the term. So the nth term is $n^2 + 2$.

Example 3.49

Find an expression for the nth term in the following sequence.

2, 16, 54, 128, ...

Solution

Write the numbers 1, 2, 3, 4 above the corresponding terms, leaving a space in between.

n	1	2	3	4
	2	16	54	128

Using COSTAS, start by squaring n.

n	1	2	3	4
n^2	1	4	9	16
	2	16	54	128

Comparing the n^2 line with the bottom line and using the TAS of COSTAS (which stands for Times, Add, Subtract), you can see there is no link between the numbers in the two lines. You don't need the n^2 line, so put a line through it.

You've used the first S from COSTAS, so now try the C (cube).

n	1	2	3	4
n^2	~~1~~	~~4~~	~~9~~	~~16~~
n^3	1	8	27	64
	2	16	54	128

Using the TAS of COSTAS (which stands for Times, Add, Subtract), you can clearly see that to find the bottom line, you would multiply the numbers in the n^3 row by 2.

So the answer is $2 \times n^3$, or $2n^3$.

The 3–5–7 sequence

This is a quicker method for some of the COSTAS sequences. It works for sequences in which the differences between terms are 3 then 5 then 7 etc.

n^2 is the sequence 1, 4, 9, 16, ... and the differences are 3, 5, 7, 9, ... so all the following sequences are based upon adding a number to n^2.

Example 3.50

Find the nth term of the sequence below.

10, 13, 18, 25, ...

Solution

The differences in the sequence are 3, 5, 7, ...

Subtracting 1 from the first term gives 9.

The nth term of the sequence is $n^2 + 9$.

Fibonacci sequences

In these sequences, each term is the sum of the two previous terms.

You will not be asked for the nth term of a Fibonacci sequence, and you do not have to remember the name.

Example 3.51

Find the next three terms in the sequence below.

1, 1, 2, 3, 5, 8, ...

Solution

Adding the two previous terms in each case, the next three terms are 13, 21, 34.

Quadratic sequences

In these sequences, each term is found by multiplying the previous term by a 'multiplier'. For example, in the sequence 6, 12, 24, ... the multiplier is 2 and the first term is 6.

The general formula is first term $\times$ (multiplier)$^{n-1}$ or $a \times m^{n-1}$.

Or try OMEN where O represents the previous term, m the multiplier and n the exponent or power.

OMEN's formula is $\dfrac{a}{m} \times m^n$.

The nth term in the example above will be

$6 \times 2^{n-1}$ or 3×2^n (be careful if $\dfrac{a}{m}$ gives a fractional answer).

Exercise 3.17

1 Look at the sequence 1, 4, 7, 10, 13, ...
  a) Find the 16th term.
  b) Find which term gives the number 139.
  c) Give a formula for the nth term.

  Hint: In these questions, it is often easier to answer the last part first and use this to find the other parts of the question.

2 For the sequence 8, 11, 16, 23, 32, ... , find:
  a) the 14th term   **b)** the nth term.

3 For the sequence 5, 12, 19, 26, ... , find:
  a) the 25th term   **b)** the nth term.

4 Find the nth term of the sequence 3, 12, 27, 48, ...

5 Find the next two terms in the sequence 2, 4, 6, 10, 16, ...

6 Find the nth term in the sequence 4, 11, 30, 67, ...

6 $n^3 + 3$
5 26, 42
4 $3n^2$
3 a) 173 **b)** $7n - 2$
2 a) 203 **b)** $n^2 + 7$
  c) $3n - 2$
1 a) 46 **b)** 47th (see part c: $3n - 2 = 139$ ∴ $n = 47$)

Answers

Sequences with fractions

Example 3.52

In the following sequence, find the nth term.

$\dfrac{3}{5}, \dfrac{5}{9}, \dfrac{7}{13}, \dfrac{9}{17}, \ldots$

These sequences are very easy if you treat the top and bottom lines as two different sequences and don't try to deal with them as if they were fractions.

What would the nth term of each line be? Try to work it out before looking at the answer.

Solution

The nth term of the top sequence is $2n + 1$.

The nth term of the bottom line is $4n + 3$.

Therefore the formula for the nth term of the sequence is

$$\frac{2n + 1}{4n + 3}.$$

Exercise 3.18

For each of the following sequences, find:

a) the next two numbers in the sequence

b) the rule linking the numbers

c) the nth term.

1 7, 11, 15, 19, … **2** 2, 8, 14, 20, …

3 13, 10, 7, 4, … **4** 4, 7, 12, 19, …

5 4, 12, 36, 108, … **6** $\frac{1}{7}, \frac{4}{11}, \frac{9}{15}, \frac{16}{19}, …$

Answers

1 a) 23, 27 **b)** $+4$ **c)** $4n + 3$

2 a) 26, 32 **b)** $+6$ **c)** $6n - 4$

3 a) 1, −2 **b)** −3 **c)** $-3n + 16$

4 a) 28, 39
  b) The difference between the numbers increases by 2 each time.
  c) $n^2 + 3$

5 a) 324, 972
  b) Multiply the previous term by 2.
  c) $4 \times 3^{n-1}$

6 a) $\frac{25}{36}, \frac{23}{27}$
  b) Top row, difference increases by 2 each time.
  c) Bottom row, add 4 each time.
  c) $\frac{n^2}{4n + 1}$

If you had trouble with Algebra before you started on this chapter, try Exercise 3.1, on page 25, again to see if you find it easier.

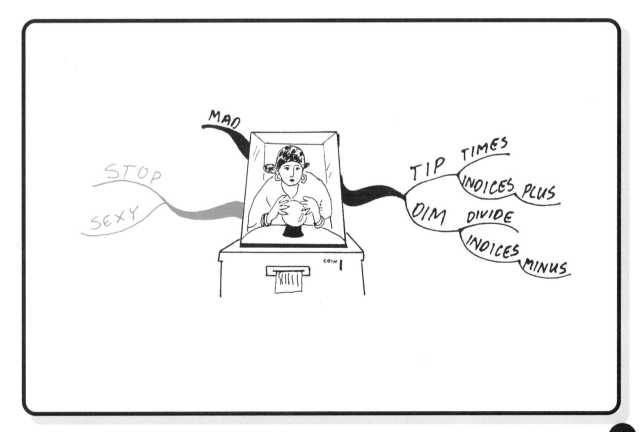

review

How much have you learnt?

Tick off each topic in the list when you are confident you can cope with it.

- ○ Explain the meaning of variable, coefficient and constant.
- ○ Solve simple linear equations in one unknown.
- ○ Solve simultaneous equations in two unknowns.
- ○ Factorise algebraic expressions.
- ○ Solve quadratic equations by factorising.
- ○ Find the rule for forming a sequence with equal differences.
- ○ Find the rule for forming a sequence with unequal differences.
- ○ Find the nth term of a sequence.
- ○ Find the value of an unknown in a formula by substitution.
- ○ Rearrange formulae.
- ○ Make expressions and equations from statements.

4

Graphs and inequalities

Do these containers have you over a barrel?

Graph recognition

Gradient

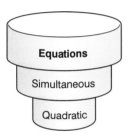
Equations
Simultaneous
Quadratic

Inequalities and Regions

preview

By the end of this chapter you will be able to:

- **solve simultaneous equations graphically**

- **interpret a straight-line graph involving two variables**

- **calculate and interpret the gradient of a straight-line graph**

- **calculate and interpret the y-intercept on a straight-line graph**

- **find a set of values to satisfy an inequality**

- **show regions on a graph that satisfy a set of inequalities**

- **match simple graphs and their equations**

- **match rates of flow in containers with their graphs**

How much do you know already?

Exercise 4.1

1 Complete the following table for $y = 2x - 3$.

x	0	1	2	3	4
y					

2 By adding a suitable line to this graph, solve the following simultaneous equations.

$y = 2x$
$x + y = 6$

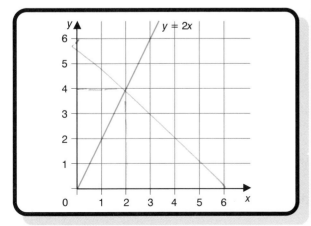

3 The graph below illustrates a family's telephone expenses.

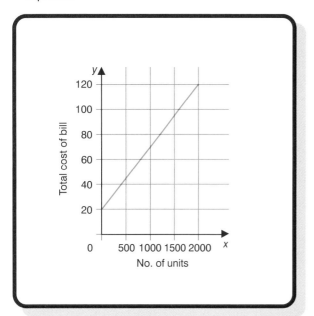

a) If the bill is £80.00, how many units were used?
b) Find the gradient of the graph.
c) What does this gradient represent?

4 From the graph below, solve $x^2 - 2x = 5$. Give both answers correct to 1 d.p.

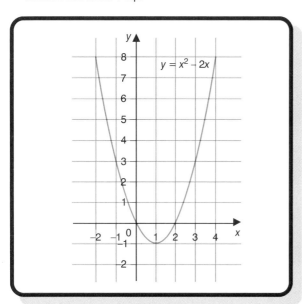

5 Find the set of values of x for which:
a) $3 - x > 4 - 2x$
b) $x^2 < 25$

6 Indicate the region R which satisfies the following inequalities.
$x + y \leqslant 7$
$2y \geqslant x + 2$
$x \geqslant 1$

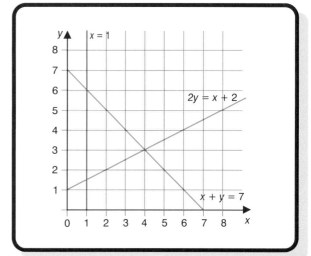

7 Match each equation to its graph.
a) $y = -x^2$
b) $y = x + 1$
c) $x + y = 3$
d) $y = x^3$

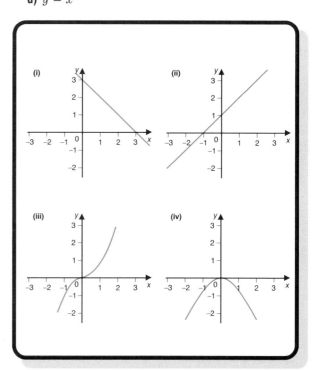

8 Liquid flows into some containers at a constant rate.
Sketch the graph of the depth of liquid against time for the following containers.

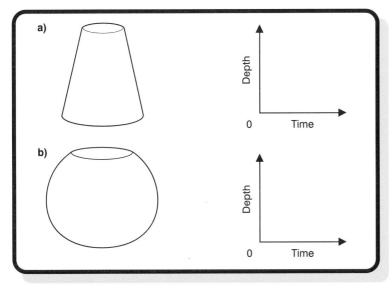

a)

b)

How did you get on?

All or most of them right?

Well done! You should be able to solve any question of the type shown above that you might find on your exam paper, but it's a good idea to flip through the rest of the exercises in this chapter just to make sure.

Half or more right?

It shouldn't take you long to fill in the gaps. Just work through the parts of the chapter which you need.

Don't even ask?

This is a short chapter and if you stay positive, you'll improve your score.

Answers

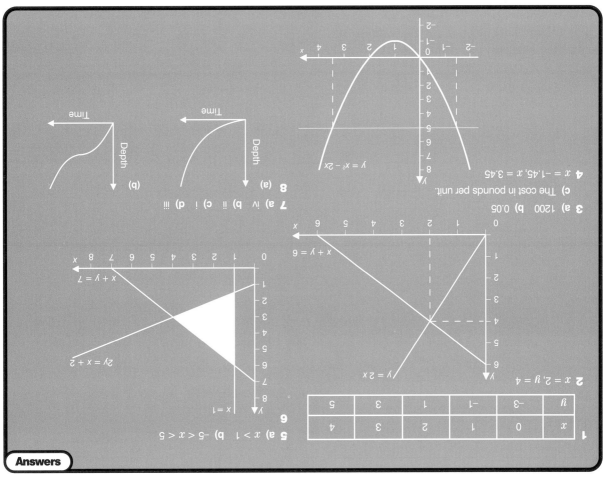

1

x	-3	-1	1	3	5
y	0	1	2	3	4

2 $x = 2$, $y = 4$

3 a) 1200 **b)** 0.05
  c) The cost in pounds per unit.

4 $x = -1.45$, $x = 3.45$

5 a) $x > 1$ **b)** $-5 < x < 5$

6

7 a) iv **b)** ii **c)** i **d)** iii

8 (a) **(b)**

4

Vases and vessels

In exams, you are often asked to recognise or draw graphs which describe the depth of liquid in a container when it is filled at a constant rate. Occasionally you are given the graph and asked to draw the container.

The rate of increase of the height depends on the cross-sectional area. The wider the cross-sectional area, the slower the rate at which the height increases.

Cylinders

Cylinders have a constant cross-section. They stay the same width all the way up and do not get narrower or wider. Therefore the rate of increase in height is constant.

Other common shapes

Here are the shapes that often come up. Get to know their graphs.

Gradients

The gradient of a line is also known as the **slope** of the line. If a line has a gradient of 2 units, then for every one unit you go along, you go up two.

Finding the gradient of a straight line

Two for the price of one, from Madam Attix!

Pick two points on the line, and construct a right-angled triangle.

> ☾ Madam Attix Says:
>
> ○ To find the gradient, GRADients are gradUAL. GRADients are Up
>
> ❊ over ALong.

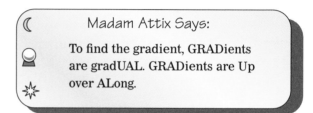

$$\text{GRADUAL GRADient} = \frac{\text{Up}}{\text{ALong}}$$

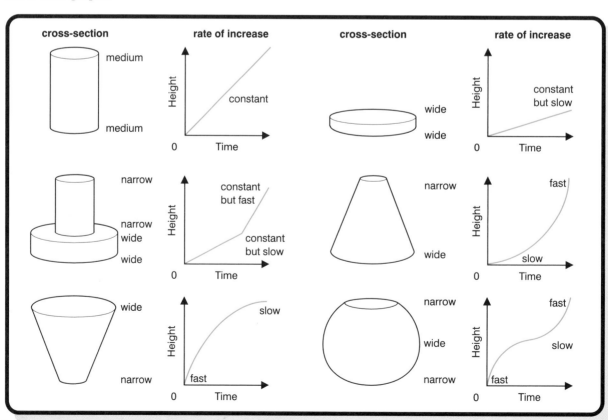

If you find this hard to remember, Madam Attix has another saying.

> ☾ Madam Attix Says:
> ☺ Gradients are GROTty, or Gradients are
> Rise (i.e. how much you go up or down)
> Over (divided by)
> ✷ Tread (how much you go along).

$$\text{GROTty Gradient} = \frac{\text{Rise}}{\text{Tread}}$$

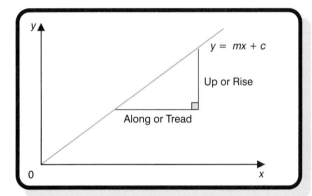

Remember: If the line slopes down, the gradient is negative.

Remember **N** for negative correlation.

The gradient and equation of a line

You may have seen the equation $y = mx + c$.

In this equation, m stands for the gradient and c is the y-**intercept**, or the point where the line crosses the y-axis.

The examiner may use different letters, e.g. $y = ax + b$. Do not be put off by this. The letter or number with the x always stands for the gradient and the letter or number on its own gives the y-intercept.

If lines are parallel, they have the same gradient.

Example 4.1

Find the gradient and the y-intercept of the line $y = 2x + 1$.

Solution

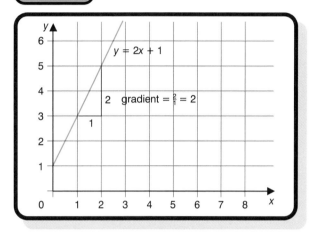

Compare the equation with $y = mx + c$.

The gradient is 2. The y-intercept is 1.

Example 4.2

Find the gradient and the y-intercept of the line $y = 1 - 2x$.

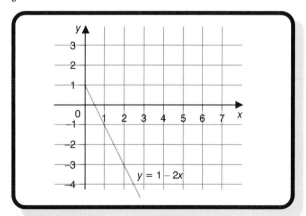

Solution

The gradient = –2. The y-intercept = 1.

Examples of this form are easier to solve if you turn them round i.e. $y = -2x + 1$.

Exercise 4.2

1 For each of the following equations, find the gradient and the y–intercept.
  a) $y = 3x + 7$ **b)** $y = 0.5x + 2$
  c) $y = 4 - x$ **d)** $2x + y = 11$

2 Which of the following lines are parallel to $y = 2 - x$?
  a) $y + x = 3$ **b)** $y = x - 1$ **c)** $y = -x - 2$

Finding the equation of a line

Example 4.3

From the graphs below, find the equations of the lines.

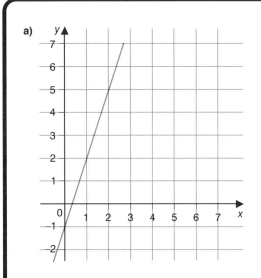

a) The gradient is $\frac{6}{2} = 3$

The y intercept is at –1, so the equation is $y = 3x - 1$.

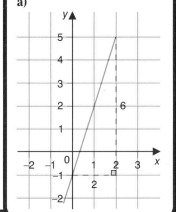

b) The gradient is $-\frac{4}{2} = -2$

The intercept is at 1, so the equation is $y = 1 - 2x$, or $y = -2x + 1$.

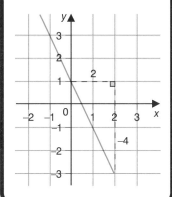

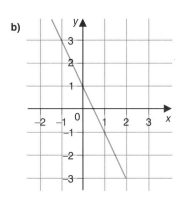

Interpreting the gradient and y-intercept

Sometimes you will be presented with a straight-line graph, and asked for the meaning of the gradient or the y-intercept.

Look at the labels on the axes, and insert the word 'per' between them as shown on the diagrams below.

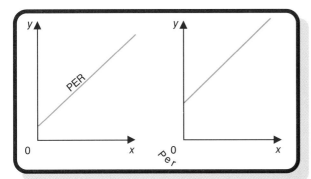

Graph 1 shows the number of pounds per dollar.

Graph 2 shows the cost in pounds (£) per unit.

Graph 3 shows the speed in km per hour.

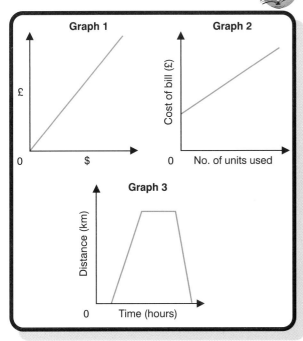

Gaynor Mark says Per means 'divided by' and it means the same as the gradient.

The y-intercept is the point where the graph crosses the y-axis. It is also the point where $x = 0$. It usually represents something like the fixed or standing charge that you have to pay, regardless of the quantity used. You generally need the y-intercept when calculating household bills, or hire charges.

> **Just to recap**
>
> The gradient of a line measures its slope.
>
> If the gradient is 0, the line is horizontal.
>
> The bigger the gradient, the steeper the line.
>
> If the line slopes down, the gradient is negative.

Do you get 'horizontal' and 'vertical' mixed up? Remember that the horizontal goes in the same direction as the horizon.

Graphical solutions to simultaneous equations

To solve simultaneous equations graphically, you simply need the values of x and y at the crossing points of the two graphs.

Sometimes the graphs are already drawn, and sometimes you need to construct them using a table of values. If there is no table given, you need to make your own. Take four values of x, such as $x = 0, 1, 2, 3$. Find the corresponding values of y.

Plot the resulting points on the given graph, and confirm that your graph is correct. If the points are not in a straight line, or a smooth curve, there is an error in either your calculations or plotting.

When drawing the line, extend it to the edge of the graph – don't just connect the first and last points.

Example 4.4

Below is the graph of $2x + y = 6$.

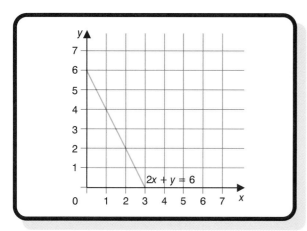

By adding a suitable line, solve the given simultaneous equations.

$2x + y = 6$

$y = 3x + 1$

Solution

Complete a table of values for $y = 3x + 1$ like this.

x	0	1	2	3
y	1	4	7	10

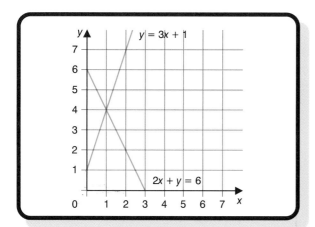

$x = 1, y = 4$

***Remember**: Simultaneous equations are SEXY, because you need to find both x and y.*

Exercise 4.3

Below is a graph of $2x + y = 8$. By adding a suitable line, solve the given simultaneous equations.

$2x + y = 8$

$y = 2x + 2$

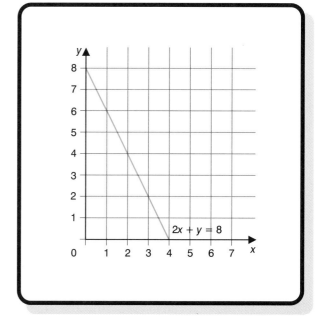

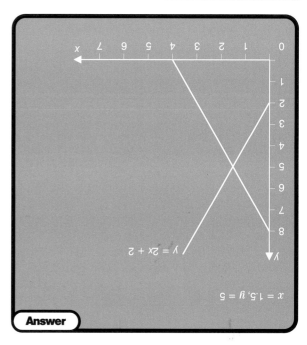

$y = 2x + 2$

$x = 1.5, y = 5$

Answer

Curved graphs

Sketching quadratics

Example 4.5

a) Complete the table for $y = x^2 + x$.

x	–3	–2	–1	0	1	2	3
y		2		0			

b) Using the table, draw $y = x^2 + x$ on the graph below.

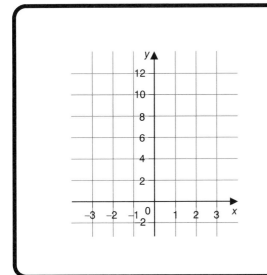

c) From your graph, find the values of x for which $x^2 + x = 3$, giving your answer correct to 1 d.p.

Solution

Complete the table of values.

x	–3	–2	–1	0	1	2	3
y	6	2	0	0	2	6	12

Note: *The values at $x = –1$ and $x = 0$ are the same. To find out what happens between these points, find the y-value when $x = –0.5$.*

If $x = 0.5$ then $y = (–0.5)^2 – 0.5 = 0.25 – 0.5 = –0.25$

Use the table to draw the graph.

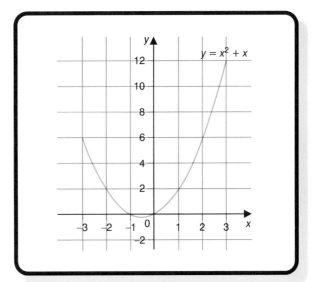

Now, to find the point where $x^2 + x = 3$, find where the graph of $y = x^2 + x$ cuts the graph of $y = 3$.

On the same graph as before, draw the line $y = 3$.

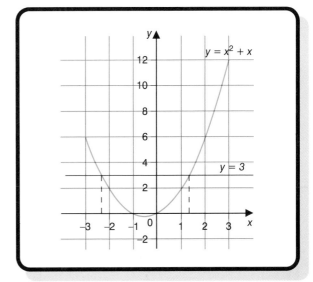

Remember: $y = 3$ is horizontal, $x = 3$ is vertical.

At the points where the two lines cross, $x = –2.3$, or $x = 1.3$.

Always join the points on a curved graph with a smooth line. Never join the points with a ruler.

4

Exercise 4.4

$y = x^2 - 5x + 3$

1 Complete the table of values.

x	−1	0	1	2	3	4	5	6
y		3		−3				9

2 Sketch the graph of $y = x^2 - 5x + 3$ on the graph below.

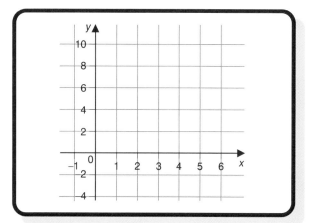

3 From your graph solve $x^2 - 5x + 3 = 0$, giving your answers correct to 1 d.p.

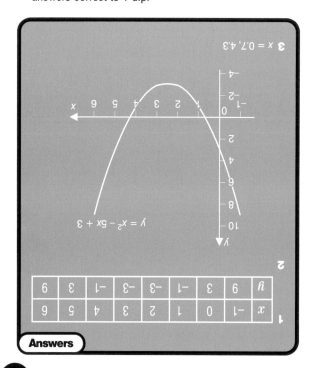

Answers

Recognising mathematical graphs

If you find these difficult to remember, try plotting a few points of the equation to see where the graph appears to be going.

Linear inequalities and regions

Linear inequalities

○ means not including

● means including

$-2 \leqslant x < 5$ means x is B≤TW≤≤N −2 and 5, and includes −2 but not 5.

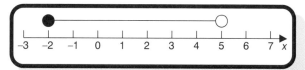

On a number line

Inequalities are very similar to equations, but with two important differences.

1 *If you swap the entire left and right-hand sides then the inequality reverses.*

For example, if Eva Rupp (e) is heavier than Honor Dyatt (h), then Honor Dyatt is lighter than Eva Rupp.

In symbols, $e > h$ or $h < e$.

2 *If you multiply or divide by a negative number, then the inequality sign is reversed. Below, $5 > 2$ but $-5 < -2$.*

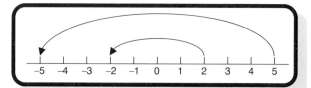

Example 4.6

1 Find the range of values of x for which $3 - 2x < 7$.

Solution

Method 1:

$3 - 2x < 7$

$3 < 2x + 7$	Taking the $2x$ over to make the coefficient positive.
$2x + 7 > 3$	Swapping the sides and reversing the inequality (rule 1).
$2x > -4$	
$x > -2$	

Method 2:

$3 - 2x < 7$

$-2x < 4$	Taking the 3 over to get the x term on its own.
$x > -2$	Dividing by -2, the inequality reverses when dividing by a negative number (rule 2).

Example 4.7

Find the largest integer for which $7x + 1 < 46$.

Solution

Solving the inequality gives $x < 6.43$.

The largest integer (whole number) that satisfies this inequality is 6.

Example 4.8

Find the range of values of x for which $2x + 1 < 3x + 7 < 2x + 16$.

Solution

Solving $2x + 5 < 3x + 7$ gives $x > -2$.

Solving $3x + 7 < 2x + 16$ gives $x < 9$.

To satisfy both inequalities, x must be B⩽TW⩽⩽N -2 and 9.

i.e. $-2 < x < 9$

The most common examples of B⩽TW⩽⩽N and ⩽⩾UTSI⩾E

Example 4.9

Find the range of values for x for which $x^2 \leqslant 16$.

Solution

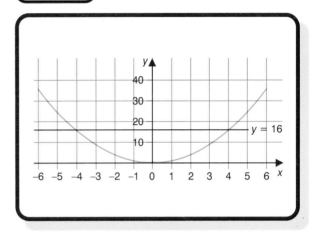

The diagram shows the graph $y = x^2$ and the line $y = 16$.

The curve is below, or less than $y = 16$ for values of x B⩽TW⩽⩽N -4 and 4.

Therefore $-4 \leqslant x \leqslant 4$.

So if the question has an x^2 with an $\leqslant$ (or $<$) sign, use B⩽TW⩽⩽N.

For example $\quad x^2 \leqslant 16 \quad$ gives $\quad -4 \leqslant x \leqslant 4$

$\qquad\qquad\quad x^2 < 25 \quad$ gives $\quad -5 < x < 5$

Hence B⩽TW⩽⩽N.

If the question has an x^2 with an $\geqslant$ (or $>$) sign, use ⩽⩾UTSI⩾E.

For example if $x^2 \geqslant 4$ then x will be ⩽⩾UTSI⩾E -2 and $+2$.

So $\quad x^2 \geqslant 4 \quad$ gives $\quad x \leqslant -2, x \geqslant 2$

$\qquad\quad x^2 > 1 \quad$ gives $\quad x < -1, x > 1$

Hence ⩽⩾UTSI⩾E.

Examples of this kind are very common on exam papers.

Example 4.10

Find the range of values for x such that $x^2 \geq 16$.

Solution

From the previous graph, it can be seen that for y to be greater than 16, x must be less than −4, or greater than +4. Therefore $x \leq -4$, and $x \geq 4$.

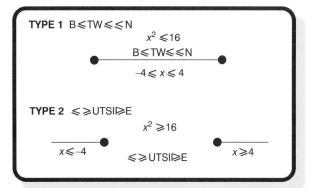

In other words, x is $\lessgtr$UTSI$\geq$E the boundaries of −4 and 4.

Exercise 4.5

1 Find the integers such that $-2 \leq x < 4$.

2 Find the range of values of x for which:
   a) $1 < 3 - 2x$ **b)** $x^2 \leq 36$ **c)** $x^2 > 25$

Answers

2 a) $x < 1$ **b)** $-6 \leq x \leq 6$ **c)** $x > 5, x < -5$
1 −2,−1,0,1,2,3

Choosing the region

Simply use A$\gtrless$OVE and B$\leq$LOW.

For example, the region $x + y \leq 6$ will be the region B$\leq$LOW $x + y = 6$.

The region $x + y \geq 6$ will be the region A$\gtrless$OVE $x + y = 6$.

Drawing the region

If the lines are not already drawn, change the inequality sign to an = sign, and draw the graph in the usual way (pages 59 – 60 of this chapter).

You usually shade the region which you *don't* want, but always **read the instructions** very carefully in case, just to relieve the examiners' boredom, you are asked to shade the required region.

Example 4.11

On the graph below, leave unshaded the region which satisfies the following inequalities.

$x + y \leq 5$

$x \leq 1$

$y \geq x$

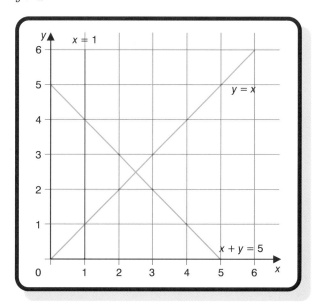

Solution

$x + y \leq 5$ the required region is B$\leq$LOW
$x + y = 5$.

$x \leq 1$ the required region is B$\leq$LOW (i.e. to the L$\leq$FT of) $x = 1$.

$y \geq x$ the required region is ABOVE $y = x$.

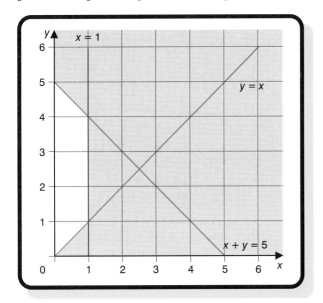

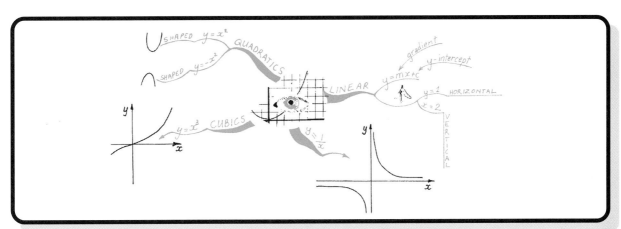

review

How much have you learnt?

Tick off each topic in the list when you are confident you can cope with it.

- Solve simultaneous equations graphically.
- Interpret a straight-line graph involving two variables.
- Calculate and interpret the gradient of a straight-line graph.
- Calculate and interpret the *y*-intercept on a straight-line graph.
- Find a set of values to satisfy an inequality.
- Show regions on a graph that satisfy a set of inequalities.
- Match simple graphs and their equations.
- Match rates of flow in containers with their graphs.

If you feel the need, go back and try the questions at the beginning of the chapter. If you are feeling confident, try the Algebra review (page 67) next.

Algebra review

1 Solve the following pair of simultaneous equations.
$x + y = 6$
$x + 2y = 8.5$

2 In the following sequences find:
a) the next two terms
b) the rule linking the terms of the sequence
c) the nth term.
    i) 8, 11, 14, 17, …
    ii) 2, 6, 10, 14, …
    iii) 1, 4, 9, 16, …

3 Factorise these expressions completely.
a) $3ab + 6b^2$ **b)** $10y^2 - 2y$ **c)** $16xy^2 + 7x^2y$

4 A boy's sister is three years older than he is, and his mother is three times as old as his sister.
a) If his age is given as n years, write down in terms of n the ages of:
    i) his sister   **ii)** his mother.
b) If the total of their ages is 67 years, form an equation in n, and simplify it.
c) Solve the equation to find the ages of the three people.

5 $C = ab + v^2$
a) Using the above formula, find C when $a = 0.7$, $b = 0.1$ and $v = 0.03$, giving your answer correct to 3 d.p.
b) Give your answer to **a)** in standard form correct to 2 sig. figs.
c) Make v the subject of the formula.
d) Hence or otherwise find v to the nearest integer when $C = 10.3$, $a = 2.1$ and $b = 0.6$.

6 On the graph below shade the region which satisfies all these inequalities.
$1 \leqslant x \leqslant 3$
$y \geqslant 1$
$x + y \leqslant 5$

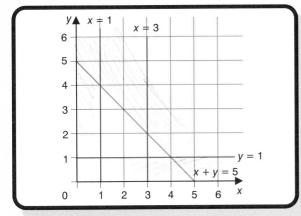

7 Write down the gradient and y-intercept of the graphs of the following equations.

a) $y = 1 - 2x$ b) $y + x = 3$ c) $y = \frac{x}{2} - 1$

8 The length of a rectangle is three times its width.
a) If its width is x cm, write in terms of x:
i) its length ii) its area.
b) If its area is 75 cm², write an equation in x and solve it to find x.

9 Solve the following quadratic equations.
a) $x^2 + 7x + 10 = 0$ b) $x^2 + 4x - 5 = 0$
c) $x^2 - 10x - 11 = 0$ d) $x^2 - 5x + 6 = 0$
e) $x^2 - 5x - 6 = 0$

10 $c = a(m - v)^2$
Find c when $a = 0.3$, $m = 0.1$ and $v = 0.6$.

11 $V = \frac{1}{3}\pi h^3$
a) Rearrange the formula to give h in terms of V and π.
b) Hence or otherwise find h when $V = 10.7$.

12 By drawing suitable lines on the graph below, solve the given simultaneous equations.
$y = x + 1$
$y = 5 - x$

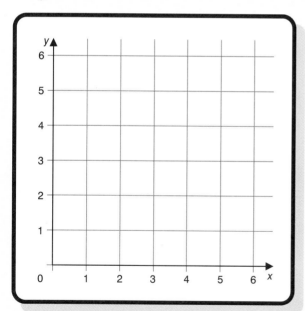

13 Find the range of values of x which satisfies each inequality.
a) $1 - 4x < 4 - 3x$ b) $x^2 \leqslant 25$ c) $x^2 > 9$

14 The graph below represents the daily hire charge for renting a car.

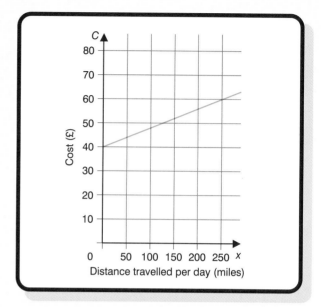

a) What is the gradient of the line?
b) What does the gradient represent?
c) Express the equation of the line in the form $C = ax + b$.

15 On the graph below, shade the area which satisfies the following inequalities.
$y \leqslant 4$
$0 \leqslant x \leqslant 3$
$x + y \leqslant 5$

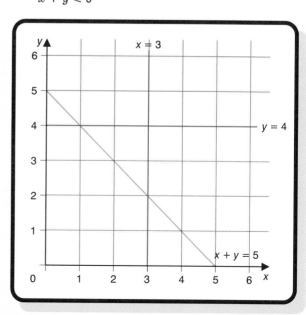

16 Match the following equations to the graphs below.

a) $y = x^3$ b) $y = x + 1$ c) $y = \dfrac{1}{x}$ d) $y = x^2$

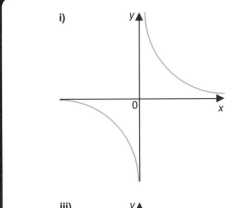

i)

ii)

iii)

iv)

17 Complete the following table of values for $h = t^2 - 2t$.

t	-2	-1	0	1	2	3	4
h		3	0				8

Hence draw the graph of $h = t^2 - 2t$ on the axes on the right.

Use your graph to solve the equation $t^2 - 2t = 2$, giving your answer correct to 1 d.p.

18 The cost (c) of a function is given as £80 to hire the hall plus £22.50 per guest.
  a) If the number of guests is x, write an equation in c and x.
  b) Use your equation to find the cost of a function for 50 guests.
  c) Rearrange your equation to make x the subject.
  d) If a function cost £2105, how many guests were present?

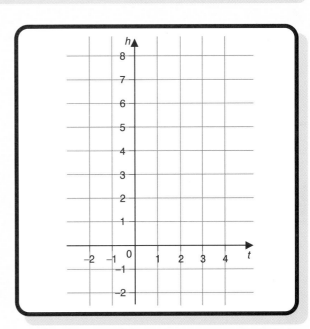

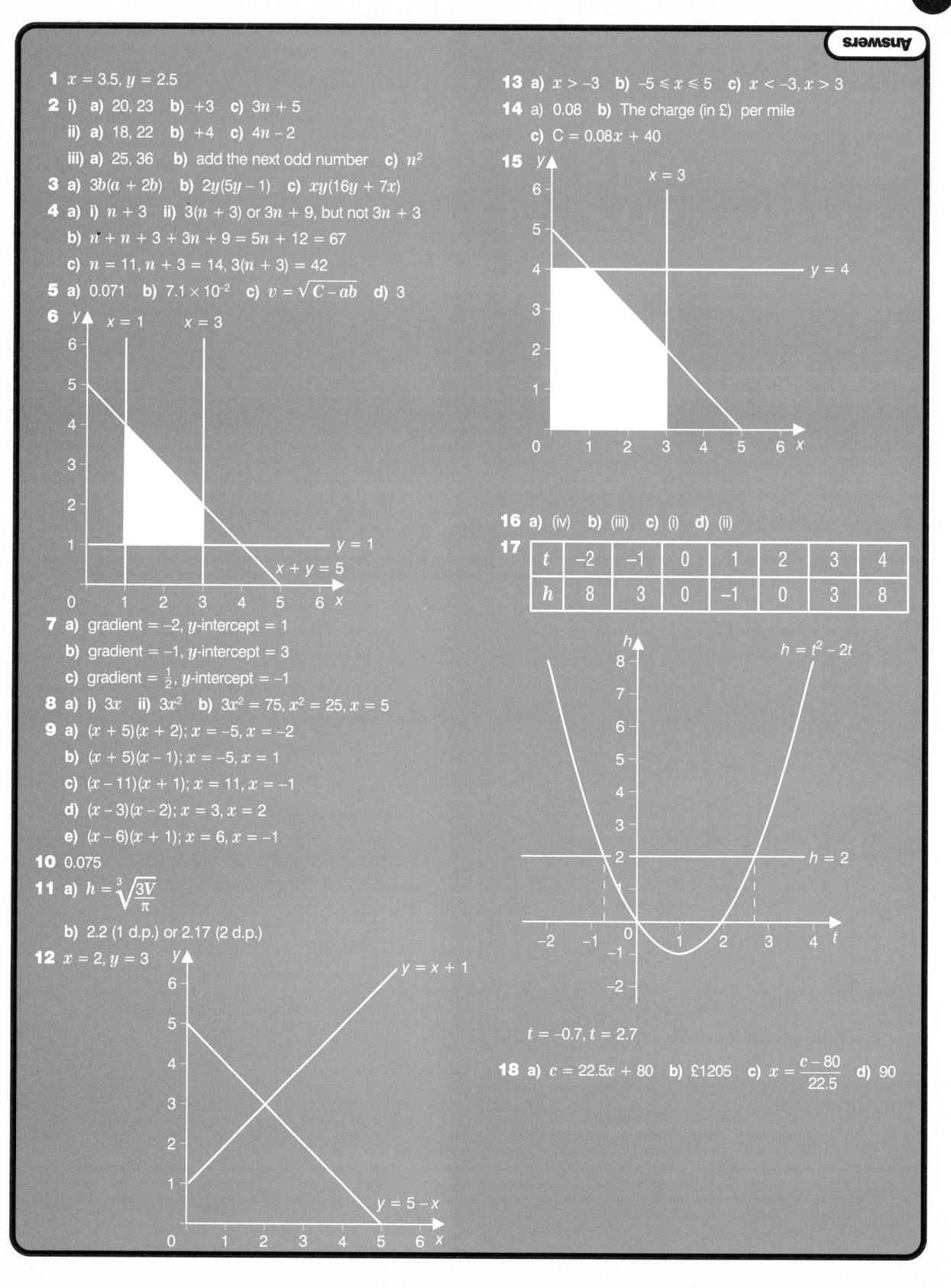

1 $x = 3.5, y = 2.5$

2 i) a) 20, 23 **b)** +3 **c)** $3n + 5$

   ii) a) 18, 22 **b)** +4 **c)** $4n - 2$

   iii) a) 25, 36 **b)** add the next odd number **c)** n^2

3 a) $3b(a + 2b)$ **b)** $2y(5y - 1)$ **c)** $xy(16y + 7x)$

4 a) i) $n + 3$ **ii)** $3(n + 3)$ or $3n + 9$, but not $3n + 3$

  b) $n + n + 3 + 3n + 9 = 5n + 12 = 67$

  c) $n = 11, n + 3 = 14, 3(n + 3) = 42$

5 a) 0.071 **b)** 7.1×10^{-2} **c)** $v = \sqrt{C - ab}$ **d)** 3

6

7 a) gradient $= -2$, y-intercept $= 1$

  b) gradient $= -1$, y-intercept $= 3$

  c) gradient $= \frac{1}{2}$, y-intercept $= -1$

8 a) i) $3x$ **ii)** $3x^2$ **b)** $3x^2 = 75$, $x^2 = 25$, $x = 5$

9 a) $(x + 5)(x + 2)$; $x = -5, x = -2$

  b) $(x + 5)(x - 1)$; $x = -5, x = 1$

  c) $(x - 11)(x + 1)$; $x = 11, x = -1$

  d) $(x - 3)(x - 2)$; $x = 3, x = 2$

  e) $(x - 6)(x + 1)$; $x = 6, x = -1$

10 0.075

11 a) $h = \sqrt[3]{\dfrac{3V}{\pi}}$

  b) 2.2 (1 d.p.) or 2.17 (2 d.p.)

12 $x = 2, y = 3$

13 a) $x > -3$ **b)** $-5 \leq x \leq 5$ **c)** $x < -3, x > 3$

14 a) 0.08 **b)** The charge (in £) per mile

  c) $C = 0.08x + 40$

15

16 a) (iv) **b)** (iii) **c)** (i) **d)** (ii)

17

t	-2	-1	0	1	2	3	4
h	8	3	0	-1	0	3	8

$t = -0.7, t = 2.7$

18 a) $c = 22.5x + 80$ **b)** £1205 **c)** $x = \dfrac{c - 80}{22.5}$ **d)** 90

5

Pythagoras' theorem and trigonometry

Try your luck! Win the goldfish

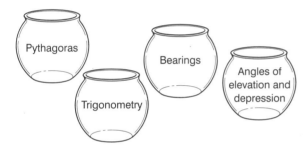

preview

By the end of this chapter you will be able to:

- **use Pythagoras' theorem or trigonometry to calculate the side or angle of any right-angled triangle**

- **recognise when to use Pythagoras' theorem and when to use trigonometry**

- **calculate and use angles of elevation and depression**

- **understand and use bearings in conjunction with trigonometry or Pythagoras' theorem**

How much do you know already?

Questions in this section will often ask you to find lengths. If the question does not specify the number of **decimal places** or **significant figures** required in the answer, use the degree of accuracy that was used in the question. For example, if the question uses one decimal place, you should give your answer correct to one decimal place (1 d.p.).

If the question asks for an angle, you should give the answer to the nearest degree, unless the question asks otherwise.

Exercise 5.1

In questions 1–8, find the length of the side, or the size of the angle, marked x.

1

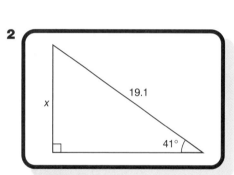

2

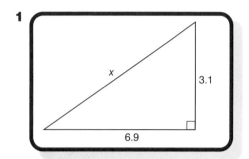

3

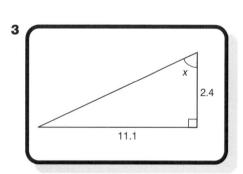

4

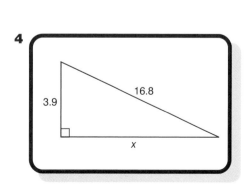

5

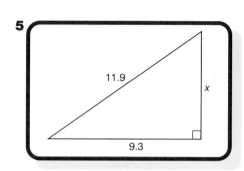

6

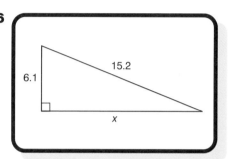

7

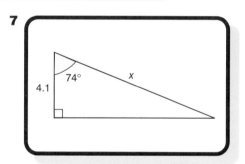

8

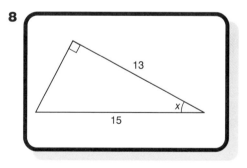

9 Lou Kout has decided to give up lion-taming for the steadier job of stiltswalking. From a safe distance of 20 m his friend, Bea Ware, watches Lou Kout practising. If the angle of elevation of Lou from Bea is 10°, and she herself is 1.6 m tall, how high above the ground is the top of Lou Kout's head?

10 Oliver Transplant wants to live nearer the show ground. At present, he lives 8 km due south of the Big Top, but is moving to a house 3 km due east of it. What is the bearing of his new home from his old?

11 Jackie Tynne is leaving. His caravan is due south of the lions' quarters. He is moving to a cottage 5.3 km away on a bearing of 073° and the lions will then be due west of him. How far away from them will he be?

12 The star performer, Jumbo, has escaped from Ivanitch's Amazing Flea Circus. Just in the nick of time Ivanitch observes him to be lurking under a leaf. Ivanitch is 1.8 m tall, and the angle of depression is 65°. How far away is Jumbo from Ivanitch's feet, to the nearest centimetre?

Answers

1 7.6	**7** 14.9
2 12.5	**8** 30°
3 78°	**9** 5.1 m
4 16.3	**10** 021°
5 7.4	**11** 5.1 km
6 13.9	**12** 0.84 m or 84 cm

How did you get on?

All or most questions right?
Well done! You probably don't need to do the next few exercises. Turn to the examination-type questions in Exercise 5.7 at the end of the chapter and see how you well you do. If you have any problems, turn back to the examples and exercises which you hoped to avoid, and work through some of them to sort out the difficulty.

Numbers 1, 4, 5, 6 right?
Fine! Pythagoras' theorem is no problem to you, but your trigonometry needs some help. Turn to page 76 where the juggling triplets will make everything clear.

Numbers 2, 3, 7, 8, 9, 10, 11, 12 right?
You are brilliant at trigonometry, but somewhere along the line you have forgotten how to use Pythagoras' theorem. Don't worry! With a little help from Madam Attix, that's easily remedied.

Don't even ask?
Never mind. It's better to find out the worst now, because Madam Attix and the juggling triplets can easily help to sort out your problems.

Pythagoras' theorem

The rule is $a^2 + b^2 = c^2$.

Identifying the hypotenuse

The **hypotenuse** is the name given to the longest side of a right-angled triangle. You will *always* find it opposite the right angle.

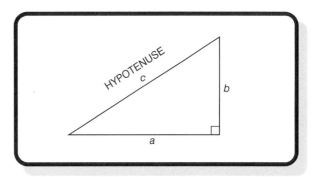

Sometimes they try to confuse you by turning the triangle round, but as long as you always **start by finding the right angle**, you can correctly identify the hypotenuse as being the side opposite it.

If you have an **isosceles** triangle (a triangle with two equal sides), you will probably not have a right angle. Don't worry! Karate Ken has the solution. Just turn it on to its odd side and chop downwards. (You're actually chopping down the perpendicular bisector.)

Calculating the hypotenuse

Once you have located the hypotenuse, it's plain sailing. Using your calculator, square the other two sides, add the results and then find the square root of the answer. Or, as Madam Attix so wisely says,

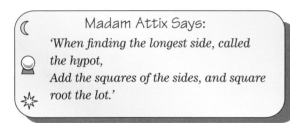

Madam Attix Says:

'When finding the longest side, called the hypot,
Add the squares of the sides, and square root the lot.'

So if c is the hypotenuse, then $c^2 = a^2 + b^2$ and $c = \sqrt{a^2 + b^2}$.

Example 5.1

In the triangle below, calculate the length of the side marked x. Give your answer correct to 1 d.p.

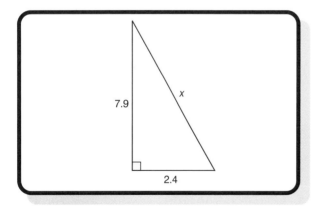

Solution

$7.9^2 + 2.4^2 = 68.17$

$\sqrt{68.17} = 8.3$

You have to be careful not to get carried away and write all the calculations in one long string, e.g.

$7.9^2 + 2.4^2 = 68.17 = \sqrt{68.17} = 8.3$

because 68.17 cannot *possibly* equal $\sqrt{68.17}$, and you may be penalised.

Exercise 5.2

In each triangle below, calculate the length of the side marked x. Give your answers correct to 1 d.p.

1

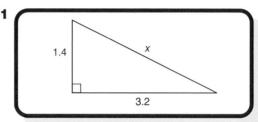

1.4

x

3.2

2

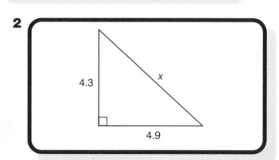

4.3

x

4.9

3

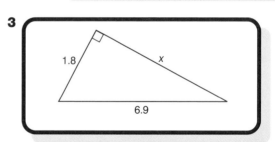

1.8

x

6.9

3 7.6

2 6.5

1 3.5

Answers

TAKE A BREAK

If you were successful in that exercise, it's time to tackle the shorter sides. If you are still making mistakes, take a short break at this point and try again later.

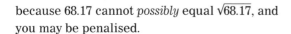
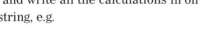

Calculating a shorter side – i.e. one that is not the hypotenuse

$$c^2 = a^2 + b^2 \quad \Rightarrow \quad c = \sqrt{a^2 + b^2}$$
$$a^2 = c^2 - b^2 \quad \Rightarrow \quad a = \sqrt{c^2 - b^2}$$
$$b^2 = c^2 - a^2 \quad \Rightarrow \quad b = \sqrt{c^2 - a^2}$$

or simply remember,

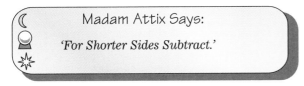

Madam Attix Says:

'For Shorter Sides Subtract.'

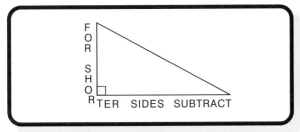

Example 5.2

In the triangle below, calculate the length of the side marked x. Give your answer correct to 1 d.p.

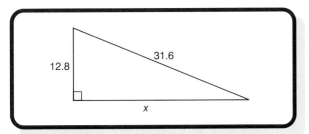

Solution

$31.6^2 - 12.8^2 = 834.72$

$\sqrt{834.72} = 28.9$ to 1 d.p.

When you are trying to find the length of a shorter side, you may sometimes find that your calculator shows the 'Error' or 'E' sign. This will happen if you start with the square of the shorter side and try to subtract the square of the hypotenuse. Your calculator will then have a negative number, for which it can't find the square root.

Safety first! Always start with the larger number.

Exercise 5.3

In each triangle below, calculate the length of the side marked x.

Give your answers correct to 1 d.p.

1

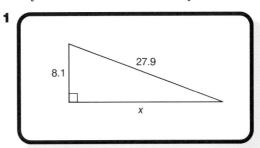

2

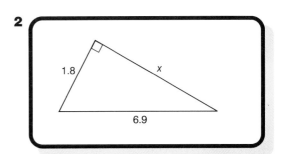

3

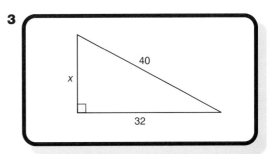

Answers

3 24

2 6.7

1 26.7

By now you should be feeling much more confident about using Pythagoras' theorem. The next exercise reinforces what you have just learnt, and gives you a chance to show off your new skill.

5

Exercise 5.4

1 On the fairground, there is a chute for children. They slide down from the top, a height of 4 m, and land on cushions on the ground. If the cushions are at a distance of 7.2 m from the base of the chute, find the length of the chute.

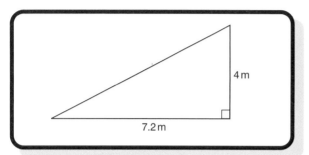

4 m

7.2 m

2 Two of the clowns do an act with a folding ladder. The ladder is 16 m long, and can be bent in half to form an upside-down V. The ladder extends to a width of 2.5 m when fully open. If a clown stands at the highest point, how high is he above the ground?

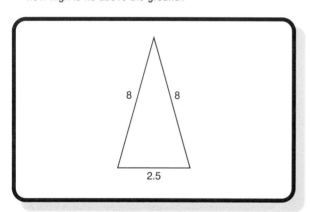

8

8

2.5

2 7.9 m

1 8.2 m

Answers

TAKE A BREAK

Now it's probably time for another short break before you and the juggling triplets tackle ...

Trigonometry

Madam Attix Says:

'Always make sure your calculator is set on 'deg' before you start your work in trig.'

Some calculators require you to press the sin, cos or tan key before the number, e.g. sin 23, whereas some calculators work the other way round and would require 23 sin. Make sure you know how yours works.

Pythagoras' theorem or trigonometry?

Whereas Pythagoras' theorem gives a relationship between **three sides** of a right-angled triangle, trigonometry involves **two sides and an angle**.

You may have learnt the trigonometry rules by using SOH CAH TOA. If you find this hard to remember, say to yourself,

Madam Attix Says:

'Some Old Hags Can't Always Hide Their Old Age.'

To show you these formulae in action, here again are Willie Droppitt and his brothers Kenny and Noel. This time they are putting the *middle* letter at the top.

S: $\sin x = \dfrac{\text{opp}}{\text{hyp}}$

O: $\text{opp} = \sin x \times \text{hyp}$

H: $\text{hyp} = \dfrac{\text{opp}}{\sin x}$

C: $\cos x = \dfrac{\text{adj}}{\text{hyp}}$

A: $\text{adj} = \cos x \times \text{hyp}$

H: $\text{hyp} = \dfrac{\text{adj}}{\cos x}$

T: $\tan x = \dfrac{\text{opp}}{\text{hyp}}$

O: $\text{opp} = \tan x \times \text{adj}$

A: $\text{adj} = \dfrac{\text{opp}}{\tan x}$

Just to recap
- The **hypotenuse** is the longest side of a right-angled triangle.
- The **opposite** is the side that is opposite (or does not touch) the angle you are using.
- The **adjacent** (which means 'next to') is the other side.

Using trigonometry to find sides

1 Write out the triplets for SOH CAH TOA, being very careful to put the *middle* letter at the top.

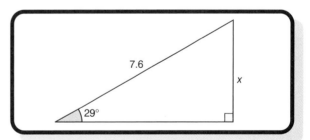

2 Look for the side which the question ignores, and cross out the triplets which contain it. The remaining triplet is the one to use.

3 Cover or cross out the letter representing the side or angle which you need to find. As usual, if the remaining letters are on the same level, you *multiply* them, and if one is on top of the other, you *divide* the top by the bottom.

Example 5.3

In the triangle below, calculate the length of the side marked x. Give your answer correct to 1 d.p.

Method

1 Label the triangle in the usual way.

2 The side not mentioned is A, so cross out the triplets containing A and keep

3 You need to find O, so cover or cross it out, and you will be left with S H.

Solution

$\sin 29° \times 7.6 = 3.7$

Example 5.4

In the triangle below, calculate the length of the side marked x. Give your answer correct to 1 d.p.

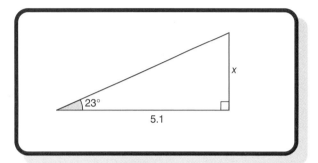

Method

1 Label the triangle in the usual way. This time the angle which you are using is at the bottom left of the triangle, so O will be the side marked x.

2 H is not mentioned, so cross out the two triplets containing it and you will be left with

O
T   A

3 You are looking for O so cover or cross it out. T and A are on the same level, so you multiply them.

Solution

$\tan 23° \times 5.1 = 2.2$

Example 5.5

In the triangle below, calculate the length of the side marked x. Give your answer correct to 1 d.p.

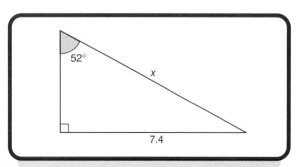

Method

When you have labelled the triangle, you should find that the unwanted side is A. Crossing out the unwanted triplets leaves

O
S   H

This time, however, the required side is H, and covering or crossing this out leaves

O
S

Solution

$7.4 \div \sin 52° = 9.4$

Check that you know how to get this answer on your calculator.

Example 5.6

In the triangle below, calculate the length of the side marked x. Give your answer correct to 1 d.p.

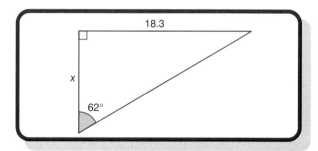

Method

When you have labelled the triangle, and crossed out the triplets in the usual way, you should have

O
T   A

As you are looking for A, you will have a division sum.

Solution

$18.3 \div \tan 62° = 9.7$

Exercise 5.5

In each triangle below, calculate the length of the side marked x. Give your answers correct to 1 d.p.

1

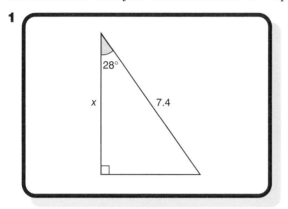

2

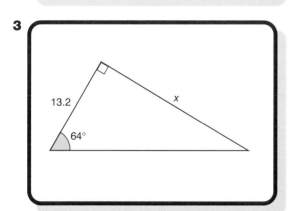

3

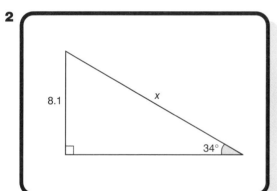

Using trigonometry to find angles

To find an angle, you must always start by finding its **inverse** sin, cos or tan, which some books write as **sin⁻¹**, **cos⁻¹** or **tan⁻¹**. To do this, you press the key which is probably in the top left-hand corner of your calculator, and labelled `inv`, `shift` or `2nd f`.

If you are getting an 'Error' or 'E' sign, or a ridiculous answer, you are probably not pressing `=` before you press `inv` `sin`, `cos` or `tan`. Also, some calculators require you to press `=` at the end, so it's a good idea to make sure how yours works, well ahead of the examination. If you still can't find where you went wrong, check that your calculator is set to degrees.

> ## Example 5.7

In the following triangle, find, to the nearest degree, the angle marked x.

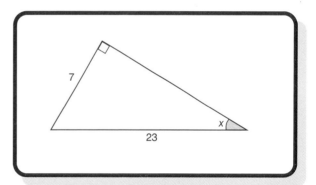

Method
1 Label the triangle in the usual way.

2 You do not know anything about A, so cross out the two triangles containing this letter. You should have

O
$S \quad H$

Solution

$\sin x = \dfrac{O}{H} = \dfrac{7}{23} = 0.304$

Angle $x = $ `inv` `sin` $0.304 = 18°$ to the nearest degree.

Example 5.8

In the following triangle find, to the nearest degree, the angle marked x.

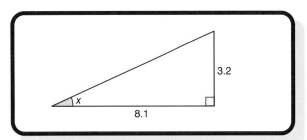

Labelling the triangle in the usual way should eliminate H.

Solution

$$\tan x = \frac{O}{A} = \frac{3.2}{8.1} = 0.395$$

Angle $x = $ **inv** **tan** $0.395 = 22°$

Example 5.9

In the following triangle find, to the nearest degree, the angle marked x.

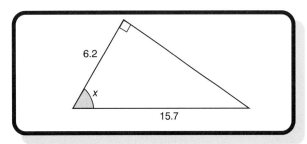

The required triplet this time is

Solution

$$\cos x = \frac{6.2}{15.7} = 0.3949$$

Angle $x = $ **inv** **cos** $0.3949 = 67°$

Exercise 5.6

In each of the following triangles find, to the nearest degree, the angle marked x.

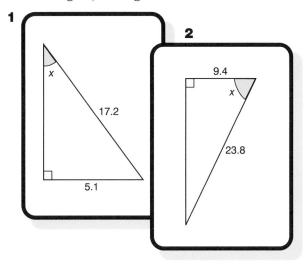

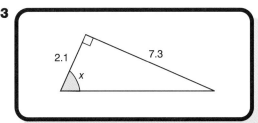

3

Answers

1 17°
2 67°
3 74°

TAKE A BREAK

Time for another break! Don't worry! There's not much more to do in this chapter, and you don't have to learn anything new to be able to deal with angles of elevation and depression, and bearings. They are merely further applications of trigonometry or Pythagoras' theorem, but they might come up in the examination.

Angles of elevation and depression

Angles of elevation and depression are always measured **from the horizontal**. Look at the horizon, and go **up for an angle of elevation** or **down for an angle of depression**.

Example 5.10

Eva Rupp is sitting 3 m away from her friend and rival Honor Dyatt who is showing off – as usual – on the trampoline. Eva's eyes are level with the trampoline and the angle of elevation is 53°.

a) How high is Honor above the trampoline?

b) When Honor looks gloatingly down at Eva, what is the angle of depression?

Solution

a) Sketch a triangle of the situation, and label the triangle in the usual way.

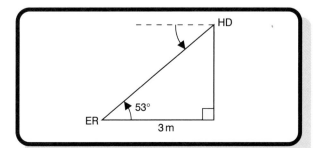

You are not interested in H, so the necessary calculation is

tan 53° × 3 = 3.98 m or 4 m

b) As you can see from the sketch, Eva's angle of elevation and Honor's angle of depression are the same.

Honor's angle of depression = 53°.

Bearings

Bearings are three-figure numbers which represent directions. They are measured as the **clockwise angle from the north**.

Bearings of 010°, 135° and 315° are shown below.

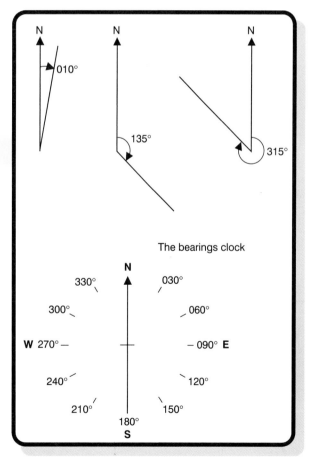

The bearings clock

Summary
- *Always use three figures.*
- *Always start from the north and go clockwise.*

Example 5.11

Everyone avoids Ivanitch when he is practising with his flea circus. If Bernie Stung is standing on a bearing of 024° from Ivanitch, what is the bearing of Ivanitch from Bernie Stung?

Solution

'From' gives the clue as to where you start.

Start by sketching the two men from the position of Ivanitch.

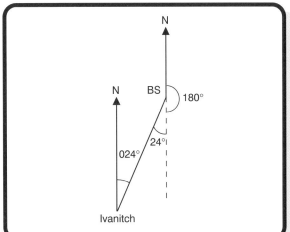

As you then have to calculate from Bernie Stung, draw a short line in the northerly direction and mark the required angle as indicated on the diagram. As both north lines are parallel, you have a pair of 'Z' or alternate angles. From north to south measures 180°, so the answer is

$$180° + 24° = 204°$$

Trigonometry or Pythagoras' theorem?

- You must have two sides to use Pythagoras' theorem.

- You must involve an angle for trigonometry.

Sometimes you can choose whichever you prefer, but remember:

TRig **IN**voles **A**ngles (TRINA).

Just when you thought you had it sussed …

Exercise 5.7

1 A ship is at S, 5 km south of a lighthouse at L. It needs to sail to a port P which is due east of L. If the bearing of P from S is 035°, find the distance that it needs to travel.

2 From the top of a cliff Albert Ross sees a rock jutting up from the sea. If the angle of depression of the rock from the top of the cliff is 15°, and the rock is 76 m from the base of the cliff, how high is the cliff?

3 An isosceles triangle has a base of 10 cm and equal sides of 17 cm.
  a) Find its perpendicular height.
     (**Hint**: Remember Karate Ken.)
  b) Find its area.

4 Dilly Gent uses a ladder 8 m long to reach a window 6.5 m up from the ground.
  a) What is the furthest possible distance between the building and the base of the ladder?
  b) What angle would the ladder make with the building?

5 Use trigonometry or Pythagoras' theorem as appropriate.

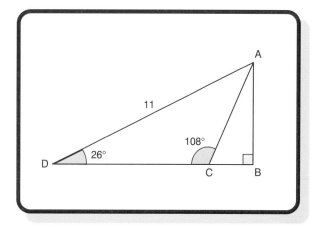

a) Find AB.
b) Find BD.
c) Write down the size of angle ACB.
d) Find AC.
e) Find CD.

(**Remember** that as triangle ACD is not right-angled, you cannot use SOH CAH TOA.)

Answers

1 6.1 km

2 20 m

3 a) $17^2 - 5^2 = 264$
$\sqrt{264} = 16.2$ cm

b) Area $= 5 \times 16.2 = 81$ cm²
(You will get the same answer if you use $\frac{1}{2} \times 10 \times 16.2$.)

4 a) 4.7 m

b) 36°
(If you have found 54°, you have found the angle between the ladder and the ground, not the wall.)

5 a) 4.8 m

b) 9.9 m

c) 72° (180° − 108°)

d) 5.0 m
(Use triangle ABC, the angle which you have just found at ACB and the length AB.)

e) 8.3 m

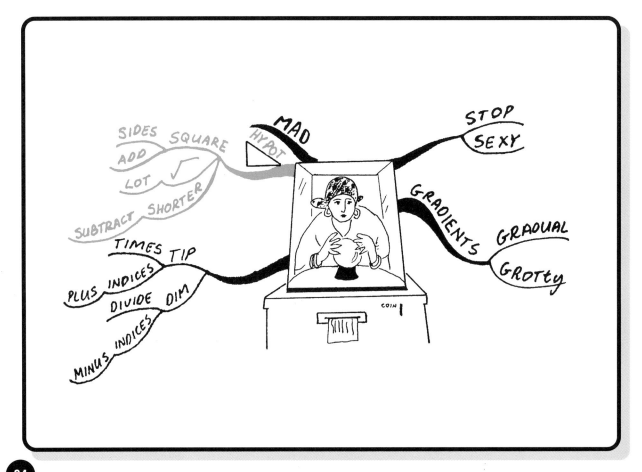

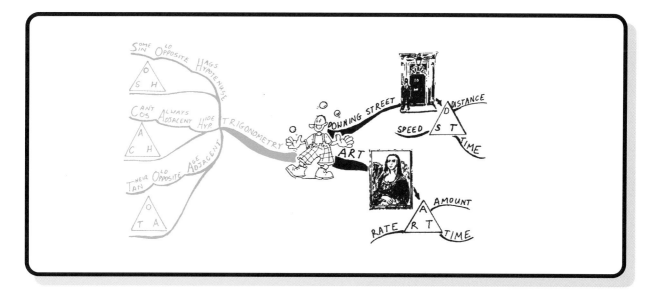

review

How much have you learnt?

Tick off each topic in the list when you are confident you can cope with it.

- ⬤ Use Pythagoras' theorem to find the length of the hypotenuse.

- ⬤ Use Pythagoras' theorem to find the length of a shorter side.

- ⬤ Use trigonometry to calculate the side of any right-angled triangle.

- ⬤ Use trigonometry to calculate the angle of any right-angled triangle.

- ⬤ Recognise when to use Pythagoras' theorem and when to use trigonometry.

- ⬤ Recognise angles of elevation and depression.

- ⬤ Calculate and use angles of elevation and depression.

- ⬤ Understand bearings.

- ⬤ Use bearings in conjunction with trigonometry or Pythagoras' theorem.

Length, area and volume

preview

By the end of this chapter you will be able to:

- identify the centre, radius and circumference of a circle

- calculate the circumference and area of a circle, given the radius or diameter

- calculate the area of a rectangle, square, triangle, parallelogram

- calculate the surface area of a cuboid

- calculate areas of shapes made up of rectangles, triangles and semicircles

- identify the cross-section of a prism and calculate its volume

- recognise formulae for lengths, areas and volumes from their dimensions

- calculate distances travelled by wheels and the number of revolutions made by a wheel in covering a given distance

- compare depths of liquids in various containers

- compare base areas of containers according to their volume or capacity

Can you see the point to all these?

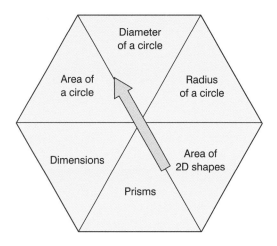

How much do you know already?

Exercise 6.1

1 Find the area of a circle of radius 2.8 cm.

2 Find the volume of a cuboid 12 cm by 30 cm by 5 cm.

3 A circle has a diameter of 16.2 cm. What is its circumference?

4 A rectangle is twice as long as it is wide.
  a) If its width is x cm, state its length in terms of x.
  b) Give its perimeter in terms of x.
  c) What is its area in terms of x?
  d) If its area is 98 cm^2, write an equation in x and solve it to find the width of the rectangle.

5 Find the area of the following shape.

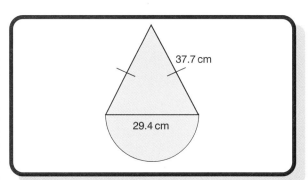

6 The letters h, l, and r, refer to lengths. State, with reference to dimensions, whether each of the following is a formulae for length, area, volume or none of these.
a) $\pi r + 2h$ **b)** $3r^3 - r$
c) $2l(r + h)$ **d)** $\pi r^2 + h^2 - (l + h)$

7 A cylinder containing 2.25 litres of a mixture has a radius of 5.5 cm. How deep is the liquid? Give your answer to the nearest cm. (1 litre = 1000 cm³)

8 A trundle wheel has a circumference of 1 m. What is its diameter, in cm?

9 How many complete revolutions would a wheel of radius 18 cm make in travelling 50 m?

10 Find the area of a circle radius 1.8 cm.

11 Find the area of the shape below.

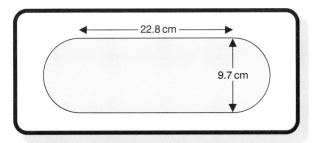

12 Compost is to be spread on a garden measuring 10 m by 6 m.

If the depth of the compost is to be 10 cm, what will be the required volume of compost? Express your answer in m³.

How did you get on?
All or most of them right?
You only need to glance through this chapter to make sure there is nothing in it which will catch you out.

Six or more right?
Look on the bright side! Six or more right means that you already know at least half of this chapter.

Don't even ask?
Keep going, and you'll make it!

Perimeter

The perimeter is the distance all round a shape. The perimeter of a circle is called the **circumference**. You should memorise the formulae for the circumference and area of a circle because they may not be given on the *Formulae and information* sheet in the exam.

Circles

These are the principal parts of a circle.

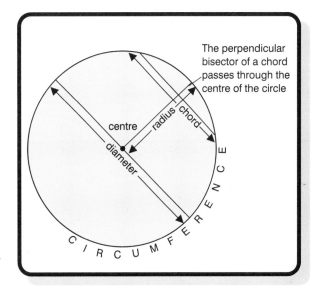

The perpendicular bisector of a chord passes through the centre of the circle

Answers

1 24.6 cm²
2 1800 cm³
3 50.9 cm
4 a) length = $2x$ **b)** perimeter = $6x$
   c) area = $2x^2$ **d)** $2x^2 = 98$ so $x = 7$ cm
5 850 cm²
6 a) length   **b)** none of them   **c)** area
   d) none of them
7 24 cm
8 31.8 cm
9 44
10 10.2 cm²
11 295 cm². This shape is the equivalent of a rectangle and a circle.
12 6 m³

The area and circumference of a circle

The area of a circle is $A = \pi r^2$.

The circumference of a circle is $C = 2\pi r$ or πd.

The formula for the area of a circle

Madam Attix Says:

πr *squarea gives you the area.*

This means the other formula must be for the circumference.

When calculating πr^2, it's safer to put r into your calculator, then square it, then multiply by π.

The formula for the circumference of a circle

From the formula for the area, πr^2, imagine the 2 running around the circumference to the front to give $2\pi r$. This is totally non-mathematical, but may help!

To remember the formula of the circumference, Willie Droppitt imagines a dog barking at a frightened cat on a table (π).

C

π d

Thus $d = \dfrac{C}{\pi}$ or $C = \pi d$

This is sometimes useful if you are given the circumference and are asked for the diameter.

Example 6.1

A circle has a radius of 4.6 cm. Find:

a) its area

b) its circumference.

Solution

'πr squarea gives you the area.'

a) $\pi \times 4.6^2 = 66.5$ cm² correct to 1 d.p.

b) If the radius is 4.6, the diameter $= 4.6 \times 2$
$= 9.2$.

$C = \pi d$ or $C = 2\pi r$

Circumference $= 28.9$ cm correct to 1 d.p.

Example 6.2 – Finding the radius when given the area

A circle has area 124.7 cm². Find its radius.

Solution

Use the formula.

$A = \pi r^2$

$124.7 = \pi r^2$

$r^2 = 124.7 \div \pi$

$r^2 = 39.7$

$r = \sqrt{39.7}$

$r = 6.3$ cm

Distance, circumference and revolutions (turns)

Examination questions often feature revolving wheels.

Distances are often written in metres and the radius of the wheel is usually given in centimetres. Be very careful to work in the same units for both.

D

C R

Remember **D**odgem **C**a**R**s.

Example 6.3

Una Sykel's wheel is of radius 20 cm. How many revolutions would it make in travelling 500 m?

Solution

Using

D

C R $R = \dfrac{D}{C}$

First find the circumference.

$C = \pi d =$ or $C = 2\pi r$ which both give
$C = \pi \times 2 \times 20 = 125.6$ cm.

Be very careful at this point, because the radius is given in centimetres and the distance in metres. It doesn't matter which units you choose, but you must work in one or the other.

$C = 125.6$ cm $= 1.256$ m

The number of revolutions is $\dfrac{50\,000}{125.6}$ or $\dfrac{500}{1.256}$.

The number of revolutions is 398 to the nearest complete revolution.

Exercise 6.2

1 Goldie Rings has a circular brooch of radius 27 mm. Calculate its area.

2 Rosa Chairz has a circular table with circumference of 408 cm.
  a) Find its radius to the nearest centimetre.
  b) Find its area correct to two significant figures.

3 Ella Von Urri's bicycle wheel is of radius 35 cm. How far will she travel in 40 revolutions? Give your answer to the nearest 10 m.

4 Nesta Tables has bought a circular tablecloth of area 17 955 cm². What is its diameter?

Answers

4 151.2 cm (if your answer was 75.6, you found the radius.)
3 90 m
2 a) 65 cm b) 13 000 cm²
1 2290 mm²

Area of shapes other than circles

By now you probably know that the area of a rectangle is length × width. Since the length and width of a square are the same, you can find the area by multiplying one side by itself, or squaring it.

Sometimes, however, you are given the area and have to work back to find a side. If you are given the area of a square, you find the length of each side by finding the square root ($\sqrt{\;}$) of the area. If you start with a rectangle, you divide the area by the side which you are given.

If the area of a square is 100 cm², each side is $\sqrt{100} = 10$ cm.

If the area of a rectangle with a length of 6 cm is 18 cm², then the width is

$18 \div 6 = 3$ cm.

Area of a triangle

$$\text{Area} = \frac{\text{base} \times \text{height}}{2}$$

or you may have learnt it as

area $= \frac{1}{2}$ base × height.

Be very careful to use the perpendicular height!

Area of a parallelogram

Area = base × perpendicular height.

Remember that the perpendicular height is the perpendicular from the base to the opposite side.

Areas of other shapes

You can usually split these up into rectangles, triangles, circles or semicircles. Then it is simply a matter of adding together all the separate parts.

You have to remember the circle formulae, but all the others should be on the *Formulae and information* sheet, which you will be given.

Surface area

Imagine that you can take the shape apart and lay each piece flat. This is also what you do when you make a net (see Chapter 7, Shapes, loci and construction). It often helps to sketch the pieces and calculate their separate areas.

A cylinder, when taken apart, is made up of two circles and a rectangle. The surface area of a cylinder $= 2\pi r^2 + 2\pi r \times h = 2\pi r(r + h)$.

The shape of a triangular prism is quite easy to remember if you think of a well-known brand of chocolate. The net is made up of three identical rectangles, with two equilateral triangles, one at each end.

Volume of a prism

A prism is a 3D shape which can be cut into identical slices. For example, if you slice a cylinder, each piece is a circle. A prism with a rectangular 'slice' is called a cuboid.

The shape of each slice is called its **cross-section**.

The volume of a prism is found by multiplying its area of cross-section by its length.

Volume of a prism = area of cross-section × length

This is easy when the question involves an obvious length. Sometimes, however, the question asks for a depth or a thickness and you may not immediately spot that this is equivalent to asking for the length. If you recognise yourself in this situation, do not despair because Willie Droppitt has a method which just might work!

V stands for volume. The word 'volume' is usually used, although occasionally you may be asked for the capacity.

A stands for the area of the cross-section.

T stands for The Other One. In place of T, you put the dimension you have not already used. This may be length, width, depth, height or thickness.

Example 6.4

a) Bart Ender makes a cocktail in a cylindrical glass of base radius 3.5 cm. If the glass is filled to a depth of 7.2 cm, find the volume of liquid in the glass.

b) Jean-Ann Tonnick does not like it and pours it into a vase in the shape of a cuboid with base dimensions 14.1 cm by 12.2 cm. How deep is the liquid?

c) Bart Ender pours the same-sized cocktail into a cylindrical glass of height 9.7 cm for Celia Fete. If the glass is completely filled, what is its radius?

Solution

a) Volume $= \pi r^2 h = 277 \text{ cm}^3$

or $V = A \times T$

b) $A = 14.1 \times 12.2 = 172.02 \text{ cm}^2$

$T = V \div A = 277 \div 172.02 = 1.6 \text{ cm}$

c) $\pi r^2 h = V$ or $A = \dfrac{V}{T} = \dfrac{277}{9.7}$

$r^2 = \dfrac{V}{\pi h}$ $A = 28.6$

$r^2 = \dfrac{277}{\pi \times 9.7} = 9.09$ $\pi r^2 = 28.6$

                       $r^2 = 9.09$

$r = 3.0 \text{ cm}$ $r = 3.0 \text{ cm}$

Mass, volume and density

Willie Droppitt brings you the density formula:
Maths for the **V**ery **D**ense!

M stands for mass. The question may refer either to weight or mass.

V stands for volume or capacity.

D stands for density.

Remember: **M**aths can be **V**ery **D**ifficult if you are **V**ery **D**ense!

Example 6.5

An object has mass of 7.2 kg and volume of 20 m³. Calculate its density, stating the units used.

Solution

$$D = \frac{M}{V}$$

$$D = \frac{7.2}{20} = 0.36 \text{ kg per m}^3.$$

Exercise 6.3

1 The base of a cuboid measures 20 cm by 13.5 cm. If its volume is 1215 cm³, find its depth.

2 Find the volume of the triangular prism sketched below.

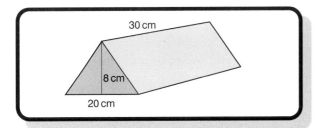

3 A cylinder holds 1 litre of water. If the radius of the cylinder is 4.5 cm, how deep is the water?

4 1 litre of fertiliser is to be spread to a depth of 4 cm. What area will it cover?

4 250 cm²
3 15.7 cm
2 2400 cm³
1 4.5 cm

Answers

- -

TAKE A BREAK

This is a good point to take a short break. When you come back, look quickly over this section once again and then have a go at the last topic in this chapter.

- -

Dimensions

In questions on dimensions you will be given expressions and asked whether they relate to length, area, or volume, or are impossibilities. These questions are easier to understand if you work in a basic unit. For convenience, we shall use cm, cm² or cm³ in the following way.

Length	cm	1 dimension
Area	cm²	2 dimensions
Volume	cm³	3 dimensions

Remember: Any measurement of length, area or volume follows the same pattern.

Don't be put off by the following rules. Read them through, then sit back and enjoy our next act on page 92, when all will be revealed.

Rule 1: Adding or subtracting like with like

- length + length = length

  Example, perimeter of a rectangle

  cm + cm = cm

- area + area = area

  cm² + cm² = cm²

- volume + volume = volume

  cm³ + cm³ = cm³

Rule 2: Multiplication of dimensions

- length × length = area

  Example, area of a square

  cm × cm = cm²

- length × length × length = volume

  Example, volume of a cube

  cm × cm × cm = cm³

- area × length = volume

  cm² × cm = cm³

Rule 3: Division of dimensions

- volume ÷ area = length

  Example, height of liquid in a container

  $cm^3 \div cm^2 = cm$

- volume ÷ length = area

  Example, finding cross-sectional area of a prism

  $cm^3 \div cm = cm^2$

- area ÷ length = length

  Example, finding length of one side

Rule 4: Adding or subtracting different dimensions gives a nonsense result

For example,   length + area = nonsense!

volume + area = nonsense!

If you can, work with the expressions alone. The diagrams are often confusing and unnecessary.

Introducing our famously frantic and flamboyant fire eater, the one and only Bernie Stung

Bernie Stung does two jobs.

1 Burns away all the numbers, including fractions and πs. These have no effect on the dimensions. For example, whether an area is $1000\,km^2$ or $10\,mm^2$, it is still an area, regardless of size.

2 Converts all the letters that are left into their usual units of measurement, leaving the power.

For example, h would become cm

r^2 would become cm^2

l^3 would become cm^3

Then he uses the rules above to find whether the formula is one for length, area, volume or none of them.

Bernie Stung in action!

Example 6.6

You are given that l, r and h represent lengths.

State, with a reason, whether the following formulae are for perimeter, area, volume or none of these.

1 $4\pi r + 2h + l$

Bernie Stung burns away the 2, 4 and π.

Cross out all the letters or numbers which he burns.

This leaves $r + h + l$

$cm + cm + cm = cm$

The formula is one for a length or perimeter.

2 $6r(l + h)$

Bernie Stung burns away the 6.

This leaves $r(l + h)$.

$cm(cm + cm)$

but $(cm + cm) = cm$ which leads to

$cm(cm) = cm \times cm = cm^2 = area$

The formula is one for an area.

3 $\frac{3}{4}lh - 2\pi r^2$

Bernie Stung burns away the $\frac{3}{4}$ and the 2π.

This leaves $lh - r^2$

$cm \times cm - cm^2$

$cm^2 - cm^2 = cm^2 = area$

The formula is one for an area.

4 $\dfrac{6\pi r^3}{r}$

Bernie Stung burns away 6π.

This leaves $r^3 \div r = r^2 = $ area

The formula is one for an area.

5 $2r^3 + 4lh^2 + 2h$

Bernie Stung burns away the 2, 4 and the final 2.

This leaves $r^3 + lh^2 + h$

$lh^2 = l \times h \times h = \text{cm}^3$

$r^3 + lh^2 + h = \text{cm}^3 + \text{cm}^3 + \text{cm} = $ nonsense

6 $r^2 l^2$

$\text{cm}^2 \times \text{cm}^2 = \text{cm}^4$

This is to the power of 4, so it cannot be length, area or volume.

Chapter 2, Number, may help you to understand the principles behind the calculation of dimensions.

Madam Attix Says:

TIP   *Times* $\Rightarrow$ *Indices Plus*

DIM   *Divide* $\Rightarrow$ *Indices Minus*

length $\times$ area = volume

$\text{cm}^1 \times \text{cm}^2 = \text{cm}^3$

volume $\div$ area = length

$\text{cm}^3 \div \text{cm}^2 = \text{cm}^1$

volume $\div$ length = area

$\text{cm}^3 \div \text{cm}^1 = \text{cm}^2$

But, as was shown in Chapter 2, Number, you cannot add or subtract different powers of numbers – or units.

Now look back at those rules on pages 91–92. We hope they make more sense now. Don't worry, though, if they still seem confusing. Just keep using the Bernie Stung technique and watch your problems go up in flames.

Exercise 6.3

The letters p, q and r represent lengths. Say whether the following are lengths, areas, volumes or none of these.

1 $4\pi r^2 + q^2$

2 $6pr^2 - \pi q^2 r$

3 $2pq + 3r$

4 $2pr + q^2 + qr$

5 $\pi pq^2 \div 6r^2$

Answers

5 length
4 area
3 none
2 volume
1 area

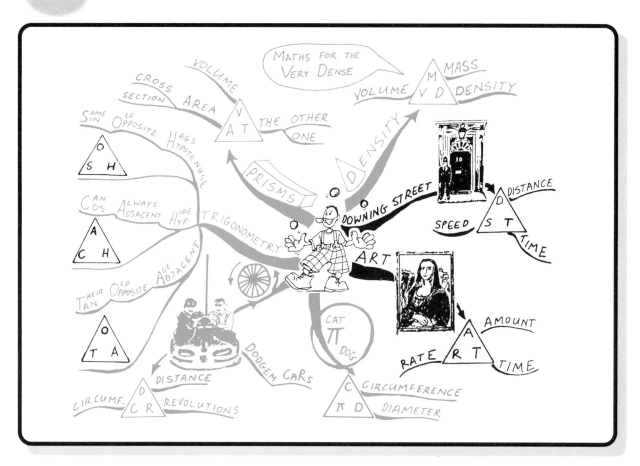

review

How much have you learnt?

Tick off each topic in the list when you are confident you can cope with it.

- Identify the parts of a circle.
- Identify the circumference of a circle.
- Calculate the circumference of a circle, given the radius or diameter.
- Calculate the area of a circle, given its radius or diameter.
- Calculate the area of
  - a rectangle
  - a square
  - a triangle
  - a parallelogram.
- Calculate the surface area of a cuboid.
- Calculate areas of shapes made up of rectangles, triangles and semicircles.
- Identify the cross-section of a prism.
- Calculate the volume of a prism.
- Recognise formulae for lengths, areas and volumes from their dimensions.
- Calculate distances travelled by wheels.
- Calculate the number of revolutions made by a wheel in covering a given distance.
- Compare depths of liquids in various containers.
- Compare base areas of containers according to the volume or capacity of liquid in them.

Shapes, loci and construction

preview

By the end of this chapter you will be able to:

- **name the different types of triangle (isosceles and equilateral)**

- **identify special angles formed by intersecting lines**

- **name and identify different types of quadrilaterals**

- **list the properties of different quadrilaterals**

- **recognise congruent shapes**

- **identify regular and irregular polygons**

- **find the interior and exterior angles of polygons**

- **state whether a polygon will tessellate**

- **construct perpendicular bisectors of lines**

- **construct bisectors of angles**

- **construct equilateral triangles**

- **construct angles of 90°, 60°, 30° and 45°**

- **draw simple loci**

- **make scale drawings**

Do some of these panels get you into a flap?

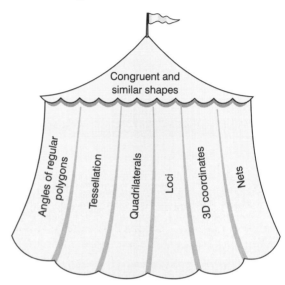

Congruent and similar shapes

Angles of regular polygons · Tessellation · Quadrilaterals · Loci · 3D coordinates · Nets

Shape and space

How much do you know already?

Exercise 7.1

1 What is the difference between isosceles and equilateral triangles?

2 Mark the angles in the diagram below which are equal to x. Give a reason in each case.

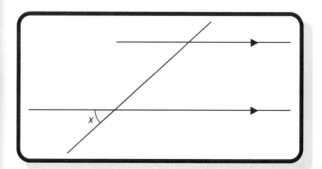

3 How many sides does a quadrilateral have?

4 Mark angle AXD.

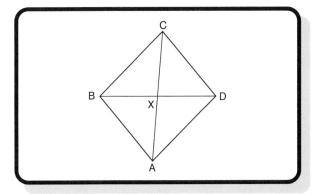

5 What is the difference between congruent and similar shapes?

6 Name the following shapes.

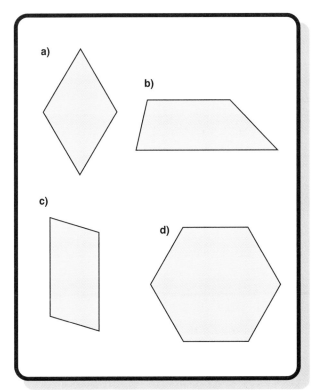

a)

b)

c)

d)

7 What is the difference between a polygon and a pentagon?

8 How do you know if a regular polygon will tessellate?

9 What is the difference between a regular and an irregular polygon?

10 Calculate the interior angle of a regular octagon.

11 From the diagram below, calculate the angles labelled x, y and z.

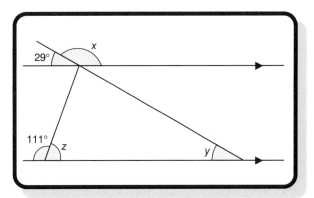

12 The diagram below represents a cage. If a monkey inside the cage can reach 60 cm, draw the locus of the points which the monkey can reach, using a scale of 1 : 40.

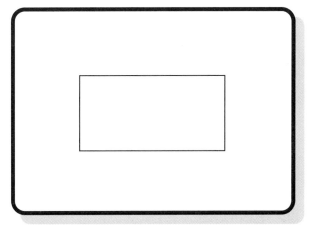

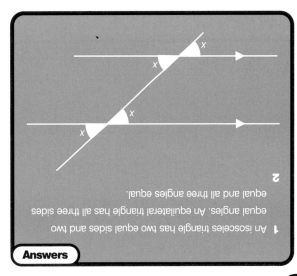

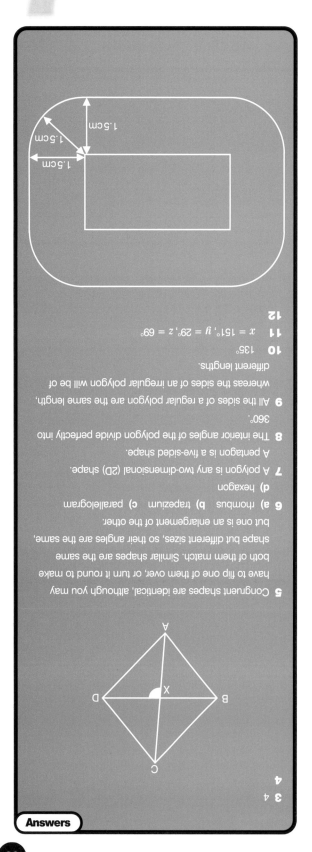

The following answers appear rotated (upside-down) on the page:

12

11 $x = 151°$, $y = 29°$, $z = 69°$

10 135°

9 All the sides of a regular polygon are the same length, whereas the sides of an irregular polygon will be of different lengths.

8 The interior angles of the polygon divide perfectly into 360°.

7 A polygon is any two-dimensional (2D) shape. A pentagon is a five-sided shape.

6 a) rhombus **b)** trapezium **c)** parallelogram **d)** hexagon

5 Congruent shapes are identical, although you may have to flip one of them over, or turn it round to make both of them match. Similar shapes are the same shape but different sizes, so their angles are the same, but one is an enlargement of the other.

4

3 4

How did you get on?

All or most of them right?
You probably don't need to work through this chapter. There are more shape and construction questions in the Shape and space review on page 114. If you have any problems with them you can come back to this chapter for help.

Five or more right?
You know most of what you need to know for the exam, but there are some gaps. You should be able to skim through this chapter, leaving out the parts you know and concentrating on where you went wrong.

Don't even ask?
This chapter is one of the easiest to learn and once again we have provided easy ways of jogging your memory.

Labelling angles

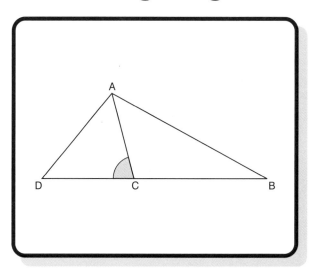

The angle marked at C may be called angle ACD or angle DCA. In some books this is written $\angle ACD$, $\angle DCA$, $A\hat{C}D$ or $D\hat{C}A$.

The marked angle at C consists of two lines AC and CD. To name the angle, you would follow the line from A to C to D or vice versa. This is to avoid confusion with the other angle at C running from A to C to B, or vice versa – which is called $\angle ACB$ or $\angle BCA$. The important letter is the middle one.

Just to recap

You need to know some special angles, and the angles formed by intersecting lines.

corresponding   opposite   alternate

Exterior angles

These are the angles at the outside of a shape, as illustrated below. If you travel right round a shape and get back to where you started, you will travel through 360°. Just divide 360° by the number of sides, and you will find the exterior angle.

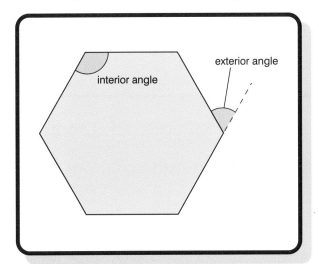

The exterior angle of an n-sided regular polygon
$= \dfrac{360°}{n}$.

Interior angles

1 Find the exterior angle by using $\dfrac{360°}{n}$.

2 As the interior and exterior angles lie on a straight line, they add up to 180°.

   interior angle = 180° − exterior angle

The angle in the centre of a regular polygon is the same as the exterior angle.

Tessellation

For shapes to tessellate, the angles at any point where they meet must add up to 360°. Designs of kitchen and bathroom flooring are often good examples of shapes that tessellate.

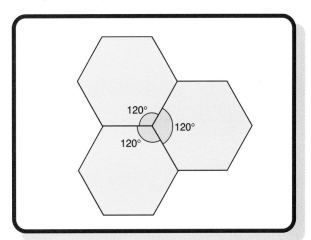

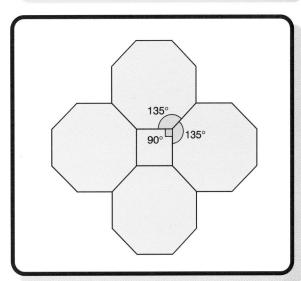

Polygons

Similar shapes

Similar shapes have identical angles, but one is an enlargement of the other. Usually, if you are asked to find the length of a side, you can use X-Direct. However, if you are asked to find the scale factor of an enlargement between similar figures, remember Madam Attix's old saying.

>
> ### Madam Attix Says:
>
> *To find the multiplier, you always put the Second number Over the FirsT – and you are SOFT in the head if you forget it!*

Example 7.1

In the diagram below, BE and CD are vertical poles. Using the lengths given on the diagram, find AD.

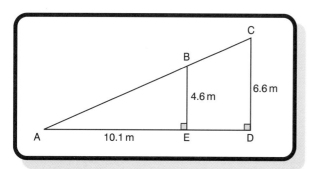

Solution

Triangles ABE and ACD are similar.

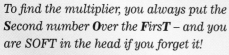

	ABE	ACD
Pole length	4.6	6.6
Horizontal distance	10.1	

$$\frac{10.1 \times 6.6}{4.6} = 14.5$$

The length of AD is 14.5 m.

In some questions like this you could use trigonometry, but this method is much quicker.

Example 7.2

Two pictures are similar. The smaller one has width 5.5 cm and length 7.4 cm. If the width of the larger one is 46.75 cm, find:

a) the scale factor of the enlargement

b) the length of the larger picture.

Solution

a) Using Second Over FirsT, the scale factor is
$$\frac{46.75}{5.5} = 8.5$$

b) The length of the larger picture is
$$7.4 \times 8.5 = 62.9 \text{ cm}$$

Alternatively you can use X-Direct.

	Smaller	Larger
Width	5.5	46.75
Length	7.4	

Length of the larger picture $= \dfrac{7.4 \times 46.75}{5.5} = 62.9$

The length is 62.9 cm.

A polygon or a polyhedron?

A polygon is a 2D shape, such as a hexagon.
A polyhedron is a 3D shape, such as a pyramid.

Just to confuse you, if the scale factor is less than 1, enlargements actually make things smaller!

Regular polygons are shapes with all sides the same and all angles the same.

Irregular polygons are shapes where the sides and angles are not all the same.

Congruent triangles

Congruent triangles are identical in size and shape, although you may have to flip one over or turn it around for the two to appear to match. You will find more on this topic in Chapter 8, Transformations.

Note: The words 'congruent' and 'similar' can describe any group of shapes. However, 'congruent' is more usually applied to triangles.

Quadrilaterals (i.e. four-sided shapes)

Square	Rhombus
• 4 right angles • all sides are equal • opposite sides are parallel • diagonals cross at right angles	(like a squashed square or a diamond) Like a square: • all sides are equal • opposite sides are parallel • diagonals cross at right angles • opposite angles are equal but angles are not right angles
Rectangle • 4 right angles • opposite sides equal and parallel	**Parallelogram** (like a squashed rectangle) Like a rectangle: • opposite sides are equal • diagonals do not cross at right angles • opposite angles are the same but angles are not right angles
Trapezium • one pair of sides parallel	**Kite** • 2 pairs of sides are equal • diagonals cross at right angles • 1 set of opposite angles are equal (shown on diagram)

TAKE A BREAK

As you have worked this far, you will probably feel in need of a break.

Watch out when Box Crusher, the circus strong man, is practising!

7

3D coordinates and nets

3D coordinates

3D coordinates are easy as long as you remember that you always read them alphabetically.

It may help to put your ruler along the lines of the shape to find the coordinates.

Always check the axes in case x, y and z are not where you expect them to be, and also remember that 3D coordinates can be negative.

Exercise 7.2

The diagram below represents a cuboid.

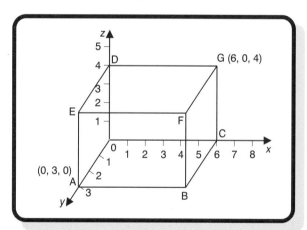

Find the coordinates of these points.

1 E

2 F

3 B

Nets

Imagine the surfaces of a 3D shape, flattened and opened out.

Exercise 7.3

Sketch a net for each of the following closed objects.

1
2

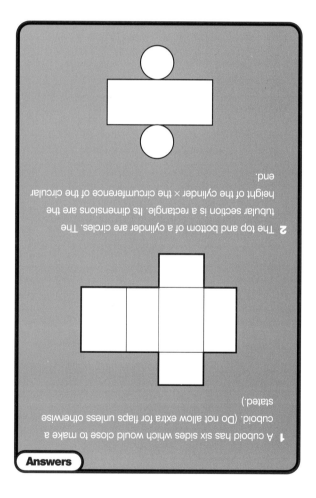

Read questions concerning cylinders and cuboids extra carefully, because sometimes they do not have a lid, e.g. waste paper bins, fish tanks, etc. There is often more than one right way of drawing the net. Always check at the end that the net you have chosen would fold up into the original shape.

Loci and constructions

What do you know already about loci and constructions?

Exercise 7.4

Answer 'yes' or 'no' to the following questions.

1 Do you know what 'perpendicular' means?

2 Do you know what 'bisect' means?

3 Can you draw a perpendicular bisector?

4 Can you draw the locus of a point from another given point?

5 Can you draw the locus of a point from a given line?

> **Answers**
>
> 1 Two lines are perpendicular when they meet each other at right angles.
> 2 To 'bisect' something means to cut it in half.

How did you get on?

'Yes' five times?
You deserve the rest of the day off!

'Yes' to fewer than five?
It's worth wading through the rest of this chapter, because loci questions often crop up in the exam, and they are an easy way of acquiring those valuable marks.

Perpendicular bisector

Gaynor Mark has the words for these.

PerpendicuLar: *at right angles*
Bisect: *cut in half*

The L reminds you that perpendicuLar Lines are at right angles.

The perpendicular bisector is a line which cuts another line in half and is perpendicular to it. It is also equidistant (i.e. the same distance) from the end points of the line.

How to draw the perpendicular bisector
Whenever you are drawing loci and constructions, always leave your compass marks on so that the examiner can tell that you have used the right method. Don't use set squares or protractors.

Example 7.3

Honor Dyatt insists that wherever she is on her tightrope, she is always equidistant from Ringo's seat and the entrance to the ring. Draw the position of the tightrope on the diagram below.

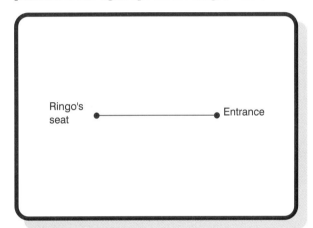

Method

1 Put the point of your compasses on one end of the line between Ringo's seat and the entrance, and open the compasses to a radius which is more than half the length of the line.

2 Using only light pressure, draw an arc either side of the line.

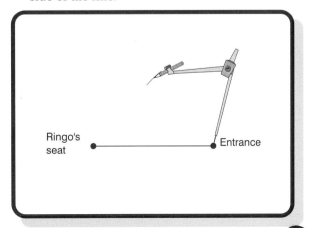

3 Without changing the radius, draw an arc from the other end. Join the two crosses to make the perpendicular bisector.

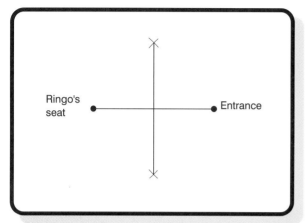

Do not use a loose pair of compasses, and always hold them from the top, so that the radius is the same for both ends.

Constructing an angle of 90°

This can be done using the perpendicular bisector method described above.

Constructing an angle of 60°

This is the same as the method used for constructing equilateral triangles.

Using any line AB, set your compasses to the same length. Put the point on A and draw an arc, and repeat for B. A line from any end point of AB to the point where the two arcs cut, or intersect, makes an angle of 60° with AB.

Yet another word for you to impress your teacher! The point where two lines or curves cross is their point of intersection.

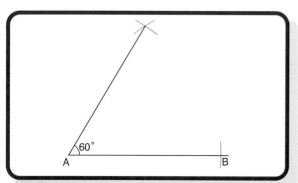

Bisecting an angle

> # Example 7.4

Karate Ken has to resolve a problem between Eva Rupp and Big Hilda Klime. They are fighting over a large piece of cake, and have asked Karate Ken to split it into two equal pieces.

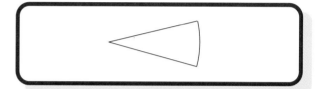

Method
1 Put the point of the compasses on the point of the angle and make an arc on each arm, at A and B.

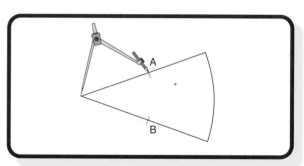

2 Move the point of the compasses to A and B in turn and make a further arc from each. Do not change the radius between drawing from A and drawing from B.

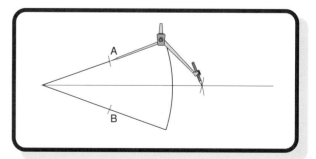

3 Join the cross to the point of the angle to make the bisector of the angle.

Remember: *You can construct an angle of 45°* *by constructing a perpendicular, then bisecting it!*

Rounded corners

Be careful to round the corners using compasses.

Example 7.5

Terry and Petra Fyde are not having much success as lion tamers. They are so frightened of Nora Nedoff that they have drawn a line which is exactly 1.5 m from her cage, which they will not cross. The cage is a rectangle, 4 m by 3 m. Using a scale of 2 cm to represent 1 m, draw the cage. Add the area which they avoid and shade it.

Solution

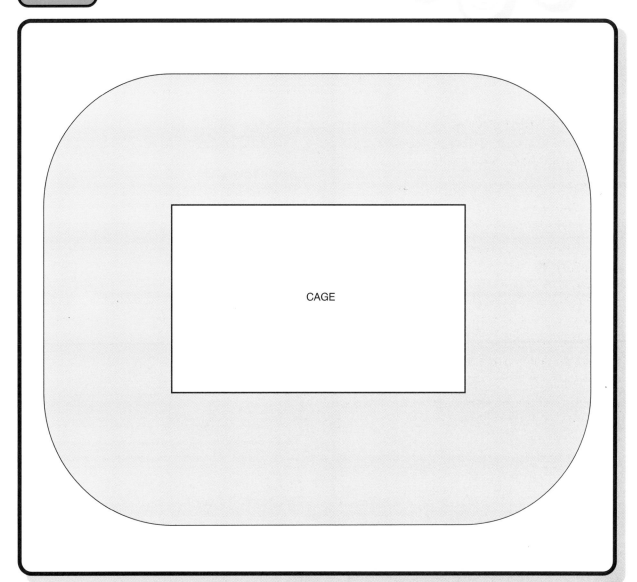

CAGE

Overlapping regions

Example 7.6

The diagram below illustrates the position of three of the fairground lights, A, B and C. They illuminate a maximum distance of 50 m, 90 m and 100 m respectively. Using a scale of 1 cm to 20 m, indicate the region which is lit by all three.

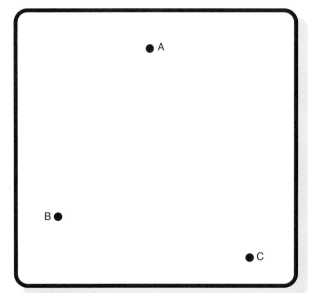

Solution

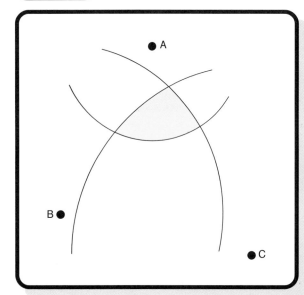

Example 7.7

The diagram shows the plan of Cliff Anger's hoopla stall. He insists that customers stand at least 4 m from his stall. Using a scale of 1 cm to 1 m, draw the area in which only Cliff may walk.

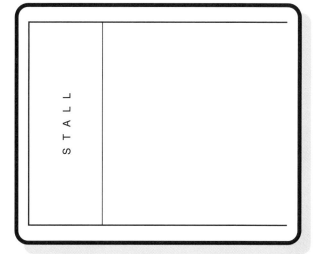

Solution

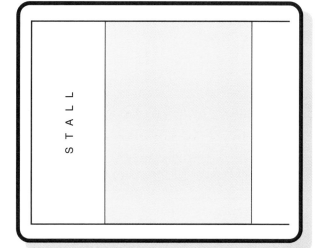

Now go back to the start of this chapter and try Exercise 7.1 again.

review

How much have you learnt?

Tick off each topic in the list when you are confident you can cope with it.

○ Name the different types of triangle (isosceles and equilateral).

○ Identify special angles formed by intersecting lines.

○ Name and identify different types of quadrilaterals.

○ List the properties of different quadrilaterals.

○ Recognise congruent shapes.

○ Identify regular and irregular polygons.

○ Find the interior and exterior angles of polygons.

○ State whether given polygons will tessellate.

○ Construct perpendicular bisectors of lines.

○ Construct bisectors of angles.

○ Construct equilateral triangles.

○ Construct angles of 90°, 60°, 30° and 45°.

○ Draw simple loci.

○ Make scale drawings.

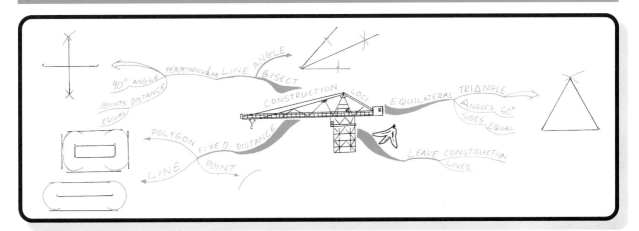

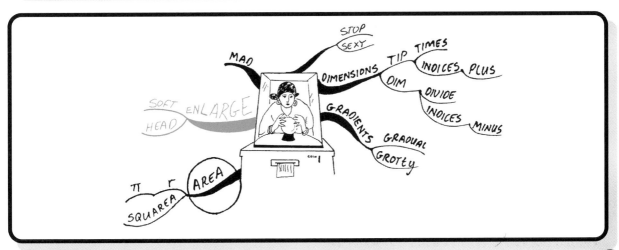

Transformations

8

By the end of this chapter you will be able to:

- **describe or draw a reflection**
  in the *x*-axis
  in the *y*-axis
  in the line *x* = *y*
  in the line *x* = –*y*
  in a line where either *x* or *y* is
  equal to any value, e.g. *x* = 3,
  or *y* = –2

- **describe or draw a translation**
  of a specified size and
  direction using vectors

- **describe or draw an**
  enlargement
  of a specified size
  from (0, 0) or any other centre

- **describe or draw a rotation**
  centred at (0, 0) and of a
  specified direction and number
  of degrees not centred
  at (0, 0)

WIN A PRIZE!	Points for each Transformation Teddy!
Translation	1
Reflection	1
Enlargement	2
Rotation	3

What do you know already?

Exercise 8.1

1 Carry out the transformations listed below, on the diagram at the top of the next page.

   a) Reflect the triangle labelled A in the y-axis. Label the reflection B.

   b) Reflect triangle A in the line $y = -x$. Label the reflection C.

   c) Rotate triangle A 90° clockwise, centred at (0, 0). Label the triangle D.

   d) Enlarge triangle A by a scale factor $\frac{1}{2}$, centre (0, 0). Label the enlargement E.

   e) Translate triangle A by a translation vector of $\binom{3}{-1}$. Label the translation F.

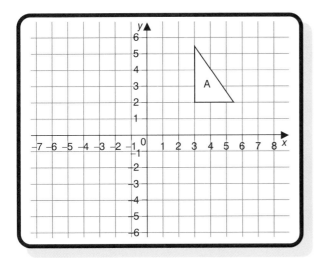

2 What single transformation would map B to D?

3 Describe fully the transformation which maps B to C.

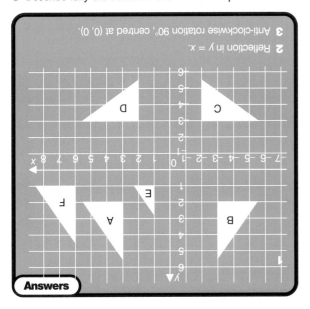

3 Anti-clockwise rotation 90°, centred at (0, 0).

2 Reflection in y = x.

Answers

How did you get on?

All or most of them right?

If you made any mistakes, just check up on the parts of the chapter which will help you to see where you went wrong, and then try the Shape and space review on page 114.

Don't even ask?

The bad news is that you will need to do some work on this part of the syllabus. The good news is that this is a very short chapter, and an easy way to pick up some valuable marks.

Identifying transformations

To get 1 mark you need to identify correctly whether the transformation is a reflection, translation, enlargement or rotation. However, you will usually score more marks by identifying the transformation fully.

Reflections

You need to identify the reflection or mirror line. This line is sometimes called the **axis of symmetry**.

It is usually easier to work out a reflection, if you get one in the exam, than to try to learn all the different combinations. To draw the image of a reflection in a line, you can use tracing paper and fold along the reflection.

Recognising reflections

These are usually obvious when the line of reflection is either the x-axis or y-axis. They are not always quite so obvious if the reflection line is $y = x$, or $y = -x$.

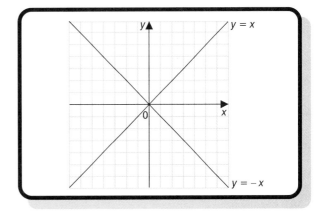

To test for reflection, take each point in turn, and count the squares or measure the distance at right angles to what you think may be the reflection line. If you are correct, the line and its image will be the same distance from the line, but on opposite sides. If the point is already on the line of reflection, it does not change.

Translations

Translation has nothing to do with foreign languages – even if at times you may think that everything to do with Maths is written in a foreign language.

A translation is a movement. The shape stays the same size and does not rotate or reflect. It merely moves its position.

Vectors

Vectors are used to describe translations. They are written in a column, with the horizontal component (the movement in the x-direction) above the vertical component (the movement in the y-direction). Because you always write x before y, they resemble coordinates, and you deserve the VC (vectors – coordinates) for getting them right.

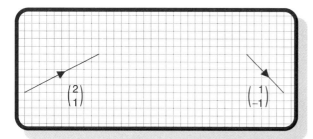

Always follow the direction of the arrow.

To gain that extra mark in the exam, you need to state correctly the translation vector.

The position of a point on an $x - y$ graph can also be written as a vector, with reference to the origin. For example, (2, 5) can be written as $\binom{2}{5}$ with the x-value (*along* the corridor) first, or on top and the y-value (and *up* the stairs) second, or on the bottom.

Remember*: They are written alphabetically, (x first, y second).*

Enlargements

To identify an enlargement, you need:

a) the centre of enlargement

b) the scale factor.

To draw an enlargement, lightly draw lines from the centre of enlargement to each point of the end of the original shape. Multiply this length by the scale factor of the enlargement. Plot the new points along your lines, measuring from the centre of enlargement.

To find the scale factor of the enlargement

If the shape and its image are already drawn, you may be asked for the scale factor of the enlargement.

Madam Attix has a wise suggestion here, too.

> Madam Attix Says:
>
> Put the **S**econd **O**ver **F**irs**T**
> (i.e. image length ÷ original length)
> and you are SOFT in the head if you get it wrong!

These helpful words can also be found in Chapter 7, Shapes, loci and constructions.

Remember*: If the scale factor is less than 1, the enlargement will get smaller!*

Finding the centre of an enlargement

Choose comparable points in your original shape and its image and join them up. Where they meet will give you the centre of the enlargement.

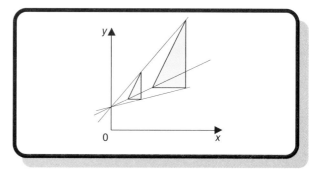

Example 8.1

Describe the transformation from ABC to A'B'C'.

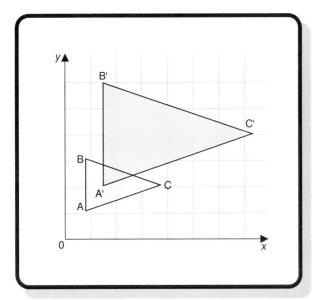

Solution

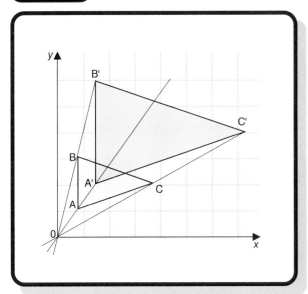

A'B'C' is an enlargement of ABC, scale factor 2, centred on (0, 0).

Enlargements are usually worth an extra two marks if you give the centre of enlargement *and* the scale factor.

Rotations

It is easier to draw a rotation if you use tracing paper. Remember, you can always ask for tracing paper in the exam if you do not already have some.

1 Trace the object.

2 Put your pencil on the paper over the centre of rotation and move the tracing paper according to the question.

3 Draw heavily over your tracing to make the image.

An alternative approach

Imagine that the axes move and not the points. This sounds complicated, but is much easier to do than you might think.

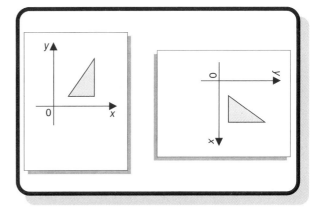

Example 8.2

On the diagram below, transform triangle T through a rotation of 90° clockwise, centred at (0, 0).

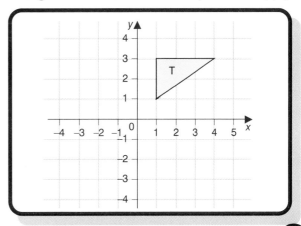

Solution

The triangle would move into the quadrant which is immediately below it.

Turn the page round so that the required quadrant is now at the top right-hand corner.

Now imagine your original triangle in exactly the same place as it was before.

Try looking at each original point and work out its new coordinates using left and right, and up and down.

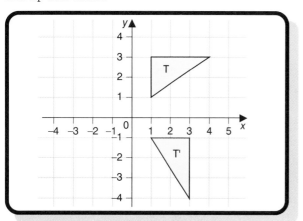

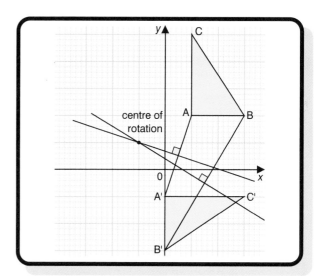

Putting it all together

If you want all the marks that are available for questions of this type, you have to describe fully any transformation that you might be given.

Recognising rotations and their centres

You can often identify a rotation by tracing over the given shape, and then anchoring your tracing at the point which you hope is the centre and seeing if you are right. Alternatively, choose two comparable points and construct the perpendicular bisector of the line between them (see page 103 if you have forgotten how to do this). Do the same to another two points.

Where the bisectors meet is the centre of rotation.

Questions involving rotational symmetry can give you three extra marks if you remember to include the centre, the angle of rotation and the direction.

Rotational symmetry may be identified by its order or fold number. You may find this confusing as it sounds like lines of symmetry. To make it clearer, a regular hexagon may be described as having rotational symmetry of order 6, or 6-fold rotational symmetry.

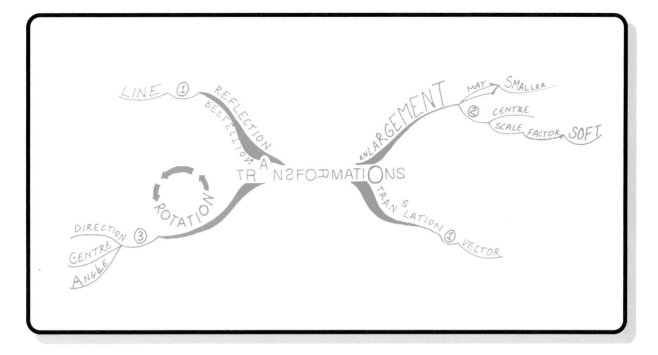

review

How much have you learnt?

Tick off each topic in the list when you are confident you can cope with it.

- ● Describe or draw a reflection
  - ● in the x-axis
  - ● in the y-axis
  - ● in the line $x = y$
  - ● in the line $x = -y$
  - ● in a line where either x or y is equal to any value, e.g. $x = 3$, or $y = -2$

- ● Describe or draw a translation
  - ● of a specified size and direction using vectors

- ● Describe or draw an enlargement
  - ● of a specified size
  - ● from (0, 0) or any other centre

- ● Describe or draw a rotation
  - ● centred at (0, 0) and of a specified direction and number of degrees
  - ● not centred at (0, 0)

If you are confident that you can now handle the topics in chapters 5, 6, 7 and 8, try the Shape and space review on page 114.

Shape and space review

1 A ladder 6 m long leans against a wall, with its foot is 2.6 m away from the wall.

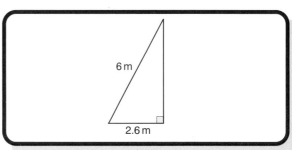

6 m
2.6 m

a) Use Pythagoras' theorem to find how far up the wall the ladder extends.
b) Find the angle between the ladder and the wall.

2 Circles of area 26 cm² are cut from card.
a) What is the radius of each circle?
b) If 24 circles are cut from a rectangle 25 cm by 30 cm, how much card is left?
c) Write this as a percentage of the original amount.

3 You are given that a, b and c refer to lengths. Using dimensions, state which could be a formula for length, area, volume or none of these.
a) $\pi a(b + c)$
b) $2b^2c + \frac{1}{4}ac^2$
c) $\pi c^2 \div a$

4 The library is on a bearing of 240° from the post office. What is the bearing of the post office from the library?

5 Describe the transformation which maps:
a) A on to B   b) C on to A   c) A on to D
d) E on to A   e) C on to B.

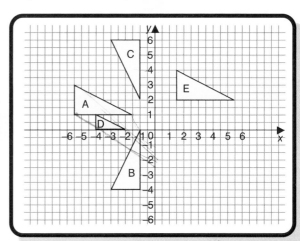

6 From a cliff top, the angle of depression of a rock out to sea is 27°. If the cliff is 45 m high, how far away is the rock from the top of the cliff?

7 Copy the diagram below to a scale of 1 cm to 1 m. It represents a garden with a tree planted at C. Grass is to be planted in the area of the garden which is nearer to C than A, but at least 4 m from the tree.

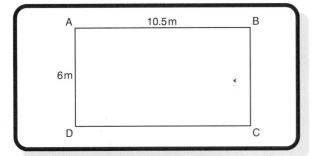

Shade the area where grass may be planted.

8 a) Name two quadrilaterals in which the diagonals do not cross at right angles.
b) Name two quadrilaterals with rotational symmetry of order 2.
c) Name a quadrilateral which always has reflective symmetry, but which has rotational symmetry of order 1.

9 What is the surface area of a solid cylinder of base radius 1.4 m and height 80 cm?
Give your answer in m².

10 Triangle DEF is isosceles. DE = 8.4 m and EF = 8 m. X is the midpoint of EF.

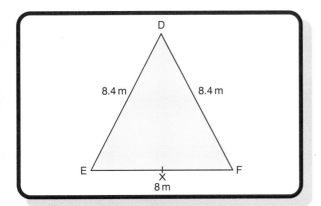

a) Find the length of DX.
b) Find angle DFE.
c) Find the area of triangle DEF.

11 a) Using ruler and compasses only, construct an angle of 60° on the line below.

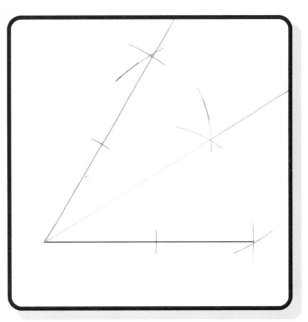

b) Bisect this angle.

Leave all construction lines on your diagram.

12 The interior angle of a regular polygon is 140°. How many sides does the polygon have?

13 a) In the diagram, BE is parallel to CD. How can you tell that triangle ABE and triangle ACD are similar?

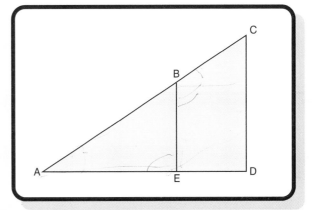

b) The length of AE = 71.1 cm, BE = 57.6 cm and CD = 80.7 cm. Using similar triangles, find AD.

14 a) Find the volume of water held by a full cylindrical glass of radius 3.1 cm and height 9.1 cm.
b) If this was poured into a cylindrical glass of radius 4.1 cm, how deep would the liquid be?

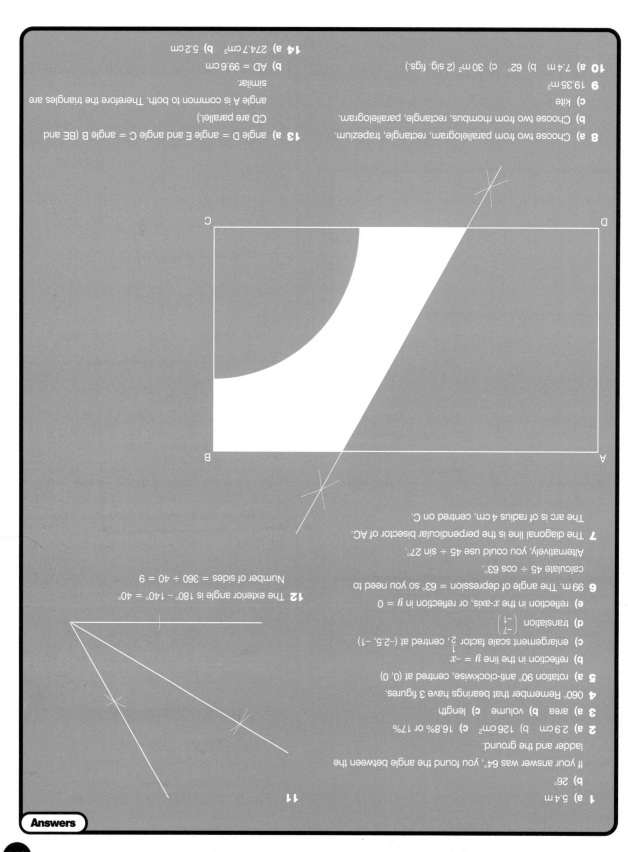

1 a) 5.4 m
  b) 26°
   If your answer was 64°, you found the angle between the ladder and the ground.

2 a) 2.9 cm **b)** 126 cm² **c)** 16.8% or 17%

3 a) area **b)** volume **c)** length

4 060° Remember that bearings have 3 figures.

5 a) rotation 90° anti-clockwise, centred at (0, 0)
  b) reflection in the line $y = -x$
  c) enlargement scale factor 2, centred at (−2.5, −1)
  d) translation $\begin{pmatrix} -7 \\ -1 \end{pmatrix}$
  e) reflection in the x-axis, or reflection in $y = 0$

6 99 m. The angle of depression = 63° so you need to calculate 45 ÷ cos 63°.
   Alternatively, you could use 45 ÷ sin 27°.

7 The diagonal line is the perpendicular bisector of AC.
   The arc is of radius 4 cm, centred on C.

8 a) Choose two from parallelogram, rectangle, trapezium.
  b) Choose two from rhombus, rectangle, parallelogram.
  c) kite

9 19.35 m²

10 a) 7.4 m **b)** 62° **c)** 30 m² (2 sig. figs.)

11

12 The exterior angle is 180° − 140° = 40°
   Number of sides = 360 ÷ 40 = 9

13 a) angle D = angle E and angle C = angle B (BE and CD are parallel.)
   angle A is common to both. Therefore the triangles are similar.
  b) AD = 99.6 cm

14 a) 274.7 cm³ **b)** 5.2 cm

9

Statistics

Are you a mean shot at statistics?

THROW BALL HERE

Averages — Mean, Median, Mode

Spread or dispersion — Range, Interquartile Range, Cumulative Frequency, Frequency Polygons

Charts — Scatter Diagrams, Pie Charts, Bar Charts

Surveys — Questionnaires, Sampling

How much do you know already?

Exercise 9.1

1 13, 7, 27, 12, 7, 10, 28, 7, 5, 11, 12, 8, 19, 12, 2.
Using the above numbers, find:
a) the mean
b) the median
c) the mode
d) the range.

2 The table below illustrates the distance between home and the town centre of a group of 75 students.

Distance in km (d)	No. of students (frequency, f)
1 km or less	6
$1 < d \leq 2$	7
$2 < d \leq 3$	15
$3 < d \leq 4$	18
$4 < d \leq 5$	10
$5 < d \leq 6$	10
$6 < d \leq 7$	7
$7 < d \leq 8$	2

a) What is the modal group?
b) Find the mean distance from the town centre to home.

preview

By the end of this chapter you will be able to:

- **find the mean, median and mode of a set of data**
- **find the range of a set of data**
- **draw a bar chart for a set of data**
- **draw a pie chart for a set of data**
- **complete a frequency polygon**
- **draw up a cumulative frequency table**
- **draw a cumulative frequency graph**
- **find the interquartile range of a set of data**
- **interpret scatter diagrams**
- **carry out sampling activities**
- **interpret results from sampling activities**
- **carry out surveys**
- **interpret results of surveys**
- **design questionnaires**
- **evaluate questionnaires**

3 Use the information in the table provided for question 2.
  a) Draw a frequency polygon.

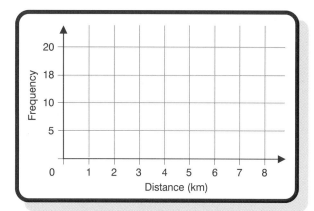

  b) Draw a cumulative frequency graph.

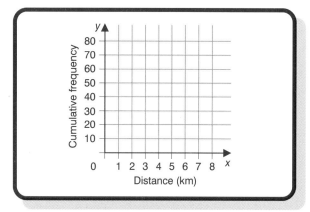

4 Using the cumulative frequency graph from question **3b)**, find the median and the interquartile range.

5 The results of a survey carried out on a sample of 450 people were displayed on a pie chart.
  a) How many people would 40° represent?
  b) How many degrees would represent 90 people?

6 The results of a group of students who sat tests in French and Spanish are given below.

French (x)	20	12	64	50	68	37	38	25	31	83
Spanish (y)	36	28	60	50	48	75	38	30	41	64

  a) Display the results on a scatter diagram.
  b) Draw the line of best fit.
  c) One student scored 56 in French, but was absent for the Spanish test. What would a likely score have been? Show clearly how you reached your answer.
  d) What kind of correlation does your graph show?

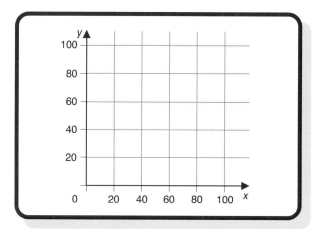

7 In a survey on homework, Candida Pinion asked ten friends, 'Don't you think that we get too much homework at the weekends?' Suggest two ways to improve the procedure.

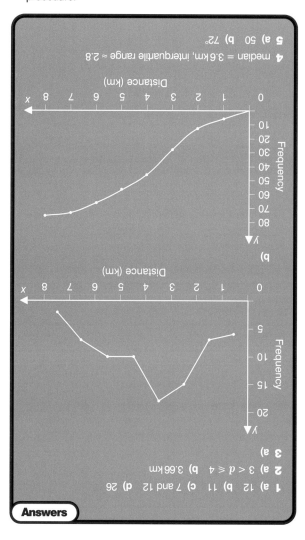

Answers

5 a) 50 **b)** 72°
4 median = 3.6 km, interquartile range ≈ 2.8
3 a)
2 a) 3 < d ≤ 4 **b)** 3.66 km
1 a) 12 **b)** 12 **c)** 11 **d)** 26

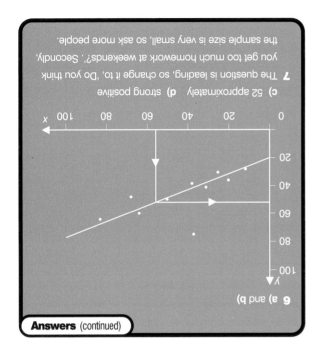

Averages and range

The mean, the median and the mode are three ways of expressing an average. The range is the spread of the data. Confused? Read on!

Mean   Add together all the values and divide by the number of values you have. (The mean is not necessarily a whole number.)

Median   Arrange the values in order from smallest to largest. The median is the middle value.

Mode   This is the most commonly occurring value. (There can be more than one mode.)

Range   Find the largest value and subtract the smallest.

The pros and cons of using the mean, median and mode

	Pros	Cons
mean	• most commonly used • easy to calculate	• can be misleading, as if one term is much bigger or much smaller than the others it distorts the mean
median	• often gives a truer picture of the situation • not so affected by extreme values as the mean	• not used very often in the real world • takes longer to calculate because values must first be arranged in order
mode	• unaffected by extreme values • very appropriate when you need to find the most common result (e.g. if you were a buyer for shoes you would want to know the most commonly bought sizes.)	• there may be more than one mode • it ignores much of the information

Answers (continued)

The following appears upside down within the answers box:

6 a) and b)

c) 52 approximately   **d)** strong positive

7 The question is leading, so do you think you get too much homework at weekends?'. Secondly, the sample size is very small, so ask more people.

How did you get on?

All or most of them right?

Lucky you – or was it just sheer hard work on your part? Either way it's good news because most exam papers are crammed with questions on this part of the syllabus and a good mark here will stand you in good stead. Look at the giant banana skin on page 123 and the Mind Map on page 128 to make sure that you won't slip up, no matter what question may be asked. If you made any mistakes, however trivial, it really is worth reading through the chapter to sort them out.

Don't even ask?

The material in this chapter carries about 20% of the total mark. Although there is a certain amount to remember, the questions are usually easy to understand.

This chapter will show you where most people lose marks in the questions on Statistics. Boxes like the one below will help you plan your work.

> **Question 1 or 2 wrong?**
> You need to brush up on averages and ranges. Otherwise go to page 120.

Getting the right answer for question 2

2 a) The modal group is like the mode. The mode is the most frequently occurring value, and the modal group is the most frequently occurring class. In this case it is $3 < d \leqslant 4$.

2 b) To answer this question you need the mid-interval value.

Distance in km (d)	No. of students (frequency, f)	Mid-interval value (MIV)
1 km or less	6	0.5
$1 < d \leqslant 2$	7	1.5
$2 < d \leqslant 3$	15	2.5
$3 < d \leqslant 4$	18	3.5
$4 < d \leqslant 5$	10	4.5
$5 < d \leqslant 6$	10	5.5
$6 < d \leqslant 7$	7	6.5
$7 < d \leqslant 8$	2	7.5

To find the mean, multiply the frequency by the mid-interval value and add the results. Then divide by the frequency.

To find the mid-interval value, Karate Ken chops the classes in two.

Distance in km (d)	No. of students (frequency, f)	Mid-interval value (MIV)	$f \times$ MIV
1 km or less	6	0.5	3.0
$1 < d \leqslant 2$	7	1.5	10.5
$2 < d \leqslant 3$	15	2.5	37.5
$3 < d \leqslant 4$	18	3.5	63.0
$4 < d \leqslant 5$	10	4.5	45.0
$5 < d \leqslant 6$	10	5.5	55.0
$6 < d \leqslant 7$	7	6.5	45.5
$7 < d \leqslant 8$	2	7.5	15.0
Total	75		274.5

Mean = 274.5 ÷ 75 = 3.66 km

> **Trouble with Question 3?**
> You need to revise frequency diagrams. Otherwise go to page 121.

Frequency diagrams

Question 3a) wrong?
If the question had asked for a bar chart, you would have drawn this.

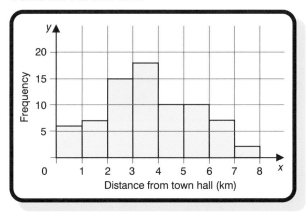

When asked for a frequency polygon, imagine the bars, and mark the midpoint at the top of each imaginary bar. Then join the points with straight lines.

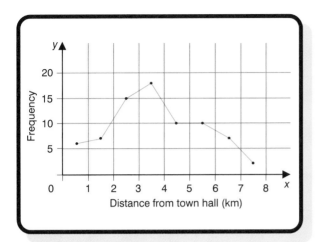

Question 3b) wrong?

To find the cumulative frequency, you accumulate (or add together, or 'roll over') the frequencies.

Distance in km (d)	No. of students (frequency, f)	Cumulative frequency
1 km or less	6	6
$1 < d \leqslant 2$	7	13
$2 < d \leqslant 3$	15	28
$3 < d \leqslant 4$	18	46
$4 < d \leqslant 5$	10	56
$5 < d \leqslant 6$	10	66
$6 < d \leqslant 7$	7	73
$7 < d \leqslant 8$	2	75

Plot the points on the cumulative frequency graph, and join them with a smooth curve.

Remember, you plot the points at the **end** of the interval and not in the middle.

> **Question 4 wrong?**
> You need to revise the method of finding the median and interquartile range from the cumulative frequency graph.
> Otherwise go to page 122.

Median and IQR

To find the median, you take the middle value of the frequency.

Usually to find the position of the median, you add 1 to the number of values and divide the result by 2. This gives the position of the median when the values are written in order.

However, as the numbers involved here are usually large, you do not need to add one first, as you usually do for the median, since the result would be almost identical. Just draw across and down as indicated in the diagram below.

The interquartile range requires the value at the **upper quartile** ($\frac{3}{4}$ way up the frequency) and the **lower quartile** ($\frac{1}{4}$ way up the frequency). The upper quartile minus the lower quartile gives the **interquartile range**.

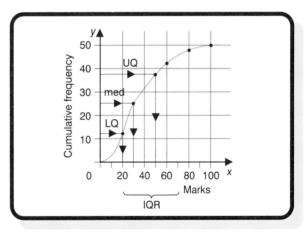

interquartile range = upper quartile − lower quartile

What does the interquartile range tell us?

The interquartile range shows how widely the central half of the sample is spread. A low interquartile range shows that the data is closely grouped together, whereas a higher figure would reflect wider differences between the data (also called a wider spread).

Example 9.1

What do these test results for classes A and B tell you?

Interquartile range	Class A	10
Interquartile range	Class B	25

Solution

The pattern of class A's results shows them to have a more similar ability level than class B – perhaps class A was streamed whereas class B was mixed ability.

Note that the interquartile range in the last example does not tell you which class had the better performance – one of the measures of the average would tell you this.

Question 5 wrong?
Just brush up on X-Direct. It's the easiest way to solve pie chart questions.

Questions on pie charts

People   Degrees

450   ✕   360

           40

$$\frac{40 \times 450}{360} = 50 \text{ people}$$

The angle of 40° represents 50 people.

People   Degrees

450   360

90   ✕

$$\frac{90 \times 360}{450} = 72°$$

The angle for 90 people is 72°.

Statistical Banana Skins

1 Mean

- This may be a decimal fraction, and may seem a ridiculous answer. For instance, the mean number of children per family is often stated as 2.4.

- If one or two values are either much bigger or much smaller than the rest, then they will alter the mean significantly.

2 Median

- If you are given some values and asked to find the median, you must first arrange them in order of size, starting with the smallest. To find the median of 7, 2, 6, 5, 4, firstly arrange them in order of size.
2, 4, 5, 6, 7
The median is then clearly seen as 5. Some people would have obtained the wrong answer by taking the middle number before they had been rearranged, i.e. 6.

- To find the position of the median value, add 1 to the number of values, and divide this by 2. For example, the middle number of 7 items is the 4th, and the middle number of eight items is halfway between the 4th and 5th. (For cumulative frequency, as the numbers involved are usually very large, simply halve the total frequency.)

- If you have an even number of values, the median is still the midpoint. For example, take the numbers 3, 7, 8, 10, 13, 19. The midpoint between 8 and 10 is 9.

- Finding the median from a table of grouped values can trip you up.

No. of people in a car	1	2	3	4	5
No. of cars	6	4	3	1	1

The answer is not 3, which is merely the middle group. There are 15 cars in total, and if they were all lined up in order with the least full cars first, the middle car would be the eighth ($\frac{15+1}{2} = 8$). The eighth car would have two passengers.

Always find the median from the frequency.

3 Mode

- You may be asked a question in which you have to compare two graphs. For instance, which of the graphs below has the higher mode?

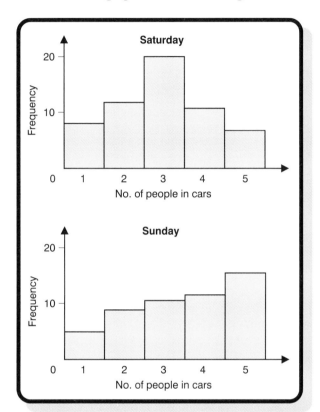

Saturday

Sunday

The mode of the Saturday traffic is 3 and that of Sunday is 5. Therefore, Sunday has the higher mode.

You have now completed most of the work on Statistics. This is a good point to make sure that you are clear about the material so far covered in this chapter.

There can be more than 1 mode — mode

The mean can be altered significantly by very small numbers. It may not be a whole number

median

To find the position of the median, take the number of values, add 1 and divide by 2

You may have to take the midpoint of two values

Just to recap

1 Can you now distinguish between the mean, the median and the mode?

2 Can you now use pie charts, frequency polygons and cumulative frequency graphs?

TAKE A BREAK

If you answered 'Yes' to the above questions, you deserve a break.

If you answered 'No', you probably need one anyway!

Question 6 wrong?

You just need to look at correlation and scatter diagrams.

Make sure that you understand the meaning of the words used.

Correlation

The **line of best fit** shows a line which is closest to the majority of the points on a scatter diagram.

When drawing a line of best fit, aim to have approximately the same number of values on each side of the line.

Correlation shows a link between the variables on both axes.

- **positive correlation** – if one variable rises, the other is expected to rise.

- **negative correlation** – if one variable goes up, the other will probably fall.

- **no correlation** – there is no link between the two variables.

For example:

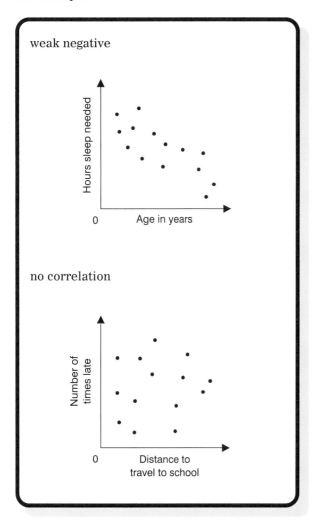

weak negative

no correlation

Sampling and surveys

A **sample** is a set of values (i.e. those given in the question). The **frequency** is how often something occurs.

Sampling

In any statistical research, it is impossible to collect data from every possible unit which may be involved. It is necessary, therefore, to take a sample, or group of the people or items that you are investigating.

Random sample

A random sample is a group selected purely by chance. You might, for instance, stop the first 20 people you meet in the street and ask them to complete a questionnaire. A drawback of using this method is that the people you meet may not fully represent the whole group. For instance, people who shop on weekday mornings may be quite different from those who shop on Saturday afternoons. For this reason another procedure is often used to find a more representative group.

Stratified random sample

Although individuals within the sample are still selected randomly, the sample itself is structured so that it represents as many groups as possible. In a survey on shopping habits, for instance, an interviewer might be asked to obtain data from a specified number of teenagers, young single adults, families and pensioners.

Examiners' questions

You are often asked to comment on a sample. There are three main points to consider.

1 **Size** – is the sample big enough?

2 **Representativeness** – are all types represented?

3 **Randomness** – is the sample biased?

Question 7 wrong?
Brush up on surveys and sampling.

Madam Attix says:
Get surveys and sampling right or you'll be **SoRR**y.

Remember, you need an ALIBI!

 Madam Attix Says:
Remember these – if not, you'll be SoRRy.

Surveys

Examiners sometimes ask you to give your opinion on surveys and questionnaires. You should comment upon the following areas.

1   **The way the question is worded**
   a) Is it a **leading** question?
      (Is it trying to push the interviewee into answering in a certain way?)
   b) Is it **ambiguous**?
      (Could the question be interpreted in more than one way?)

2   **The range of responses**
   This is less common, but you should look at ways which the interviewee can reply to see whether all possible outcomes are clearly and accurately represented.

3   **Drawing up questionnaires**
   a) Ask yourself if the question is easy to understand.
      Is the meaning clear, or could there be more than one interpretation?
      Is it ambiguous?
   b) Is the question leading?
      Does it suggest an answer?
   c) Do the answer boxes cover the full range of responses?
      Are they inclusive?
   d) Will the results be fair and unbiased?

Use the above criteria and avoid the pitfalls.

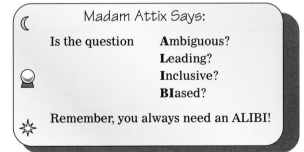

Madam Attix Says:

Is the question   **A**mbiguous?
                   Leading?
                   Inclusive?
                   BIased?

Remember, you always need an ALIBI!

Exercise 9.2

1 What kind of correlation is shown on the graph below?

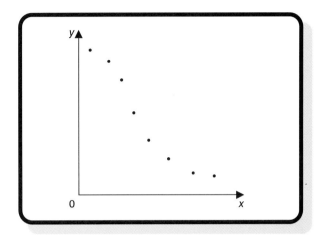

2 The results of a survey on 1440 students who completed a questionnaire on their favourite subject are given below.

Favourite subject	No. of students
Maths	108
English	300
PE	520
Sciences	124
Languages	388

Construct a pie chart to show this information. Mark the number of degrees required for each subject.

3 The following table represents the test marks achieved for a group of 50 candidates.

Marks, m	Frequency, f
$0 < m \leq 20$	12
$20 < m \leq 40$	20
$40 < m \leq 60$	10
$60 < m \leq 80$	6
$80 < m \leq 100$	2

a) What is the modal group?

b) Copy the table and complete a column showing the cumulative frequency.

c) Display the information on a cumulative frequency graph, and find the median and the interquartile range.

d) What percentage of students scored above 70%?

e) If the pass mark was 40%, how many students failed?

f) Another group which took the test had a median of 26 and an interquartile range of 35. Which class was streamed and which was of mixed ability? Give a reason for your answer.

4 Using the table in question 3, find the mean mark.

5 Using the table in question 3, draw a frequency polygon.

Answers

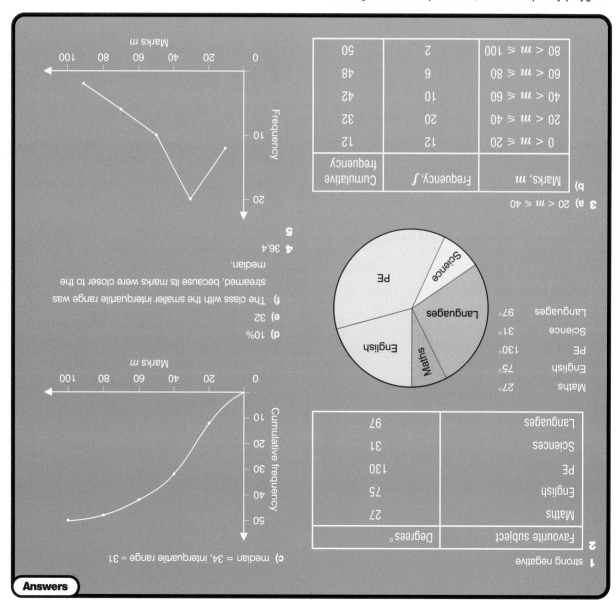

1 strong negative

2

Favourite subject	Degrees°
Maths	27
English	75
PE	130
Sciences	31
Languages	97

Maths	27°
English	75°
PE	130°
Science	31°
Languages	97°

3 a) $20 < m \leq 40$

b)

Marks, m	Frequency, f	Cumulative frequency
$0 < m \leq 20$	12	12
$20 < m \leq 40$	20	32
$40 < m \leq 60$	10	42
$60 < m \leq 80$	6	48
$80 < m \leq 100$	2	50

c) median = 34, interquartile range ≈ 31

d) 10%

e) 32

f) The class with the smaller interquartile range was streamed, because its marks were closer to the median.

4 36.4

5

The grand parade

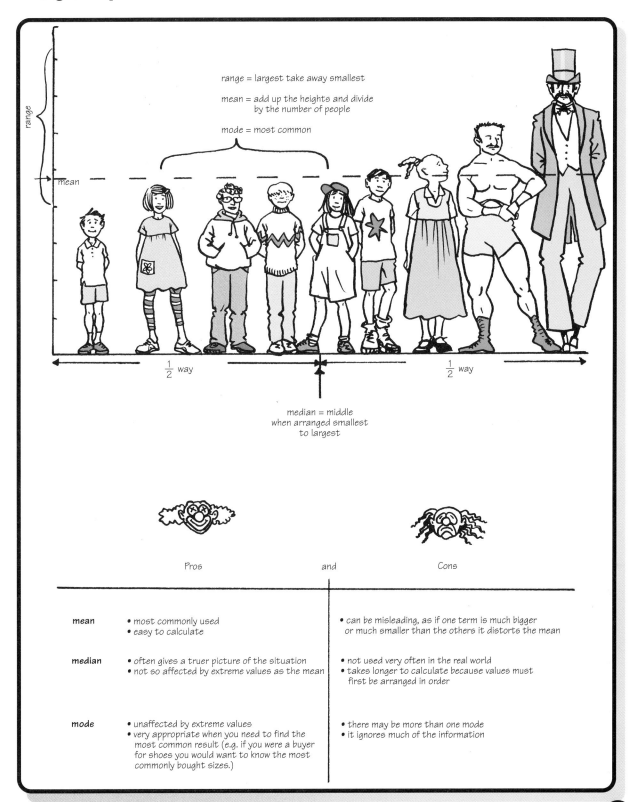

range = largest take away smallest

mean = add up the heights and divide by the number of people

mode = most common

median = middle when arranged smallest to largest

Pros   and   Cons

	Pros	Cons
mean	• most commonly used • easy to calculate	• can be misleading, as if one term is much bigger or much smaller than the others it distorts the mean
median	• often gives a truer picture of the situation • not so affected by extreme values as the mean	• not used very often in the real world • takes longer to calculate because values must first be arranged in order
mode	• unaffected by extreme values • very appropriate when you need to find the most common result (e.g. if you were a buyer for shoes you would want to know the most commonly bought sizes.)	• there may be more than one mode • it ignores much of the information

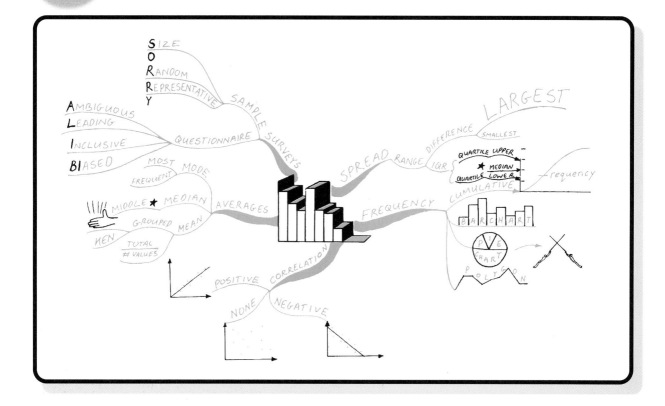

review

How much have you learnt?

Tick off each topic in the list when you are confident you can cope with it.

- Find the mean of a set of data.
- Find the median of a set of data.
- Find the mode of a set of data.
- Find the range of a set of data.
- Draw a bar chart for a set of data.
- Draw a pie chart for a set of data.
- Complete a frequency polygon.
- Draw up a cumulative frequency table.
- Draw a cumulative frequency graph.
- Find the interquartile range of a set of data.
- Interpret scatter diagrams.
- Carry out sampling activities.
- Interpret results from sampling activities.
- Carry out surveys.
- Interpret results of surveys.
- Design questionnaires.
- Evaluate questionnaires.

10

Probability preview

Probability preview

Are you holding all the right cards?

Calculating the probability of a single event	Tree diagrams
	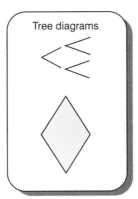

Using 'AND' and 'OR' in probability	Mutually exclusive events

By the end of this chapter you will be able to:

- **find the probability of an event with a known number of possible outcomes**

- **find the joint probability of two events that are independent**

- **construct tree diagrams**

- **identify mutually exclusive events**

- **calculate the probability of two mutually exclusive events occurring**

- **comment on suggestions about the probabilities of two events that are not necessarily mutually exclusive**

How much do you already know?

Exercise 10.1

♣ **1** In a competition, the probability of winning a prize was 0.35. What was the probability of not winning?

♣ **2** 1000 tickets were sold in a raffle. If there were 28 prizes, what was the probability of any one ticket winning a prize? Write your answer as a fraction in its lowest terms.

♥ **3** If a six-sided dice is thrown, and a coin is tossed, how many different outcomes are there?

4 Complete the following tree diagram.

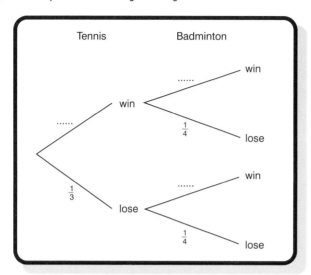

5 Vic Taurius has been competing in tennis and badminton tournaments. Using the information given in the question above, find the probability that he:
 a) wins both tournaments
 b) wins the tennis, but not the badminton
 c) wins only one tournament.

6 The probability of a member of the circus attending the acrobatics-for-the-unfit class is 0.36, and of training with the custard-pie-dodging group is 0.23. Members are only allowed to belong to one group at a time. What is the probability that a student taken at random belongs either to the acrobatics class, or to the custard pie dodgers?

7 In a box there are seven red, five blue and four green buttons. In addition, the buttons may be round, square or oval.
 a) What is the probability that a button taken at random is blue?
 b) If $\frac{1}{8}$ of the buttons are round, why can you not be sure that the probability of choosing a blue or round button is $\frac{5}{16} + \frac{1}{8} = \frac{7}{16}$?

8 Crispin Syde only likes chocolates with hard centres. In a box of 30 chocolates, 12 have soft centres, 20 are milk chocolates and 5 are foil wrapped. He takes one at random.
 a) What is the probability of choosing one with a soft centre?
 b) If he wants a chocolate to have a hard centre or be foil wrapped, is the probability necessarily $\frac{1}{6} + \frac{2}{3}$? Give a reason.

If you had a problem with a question, note which suit it belongs to.

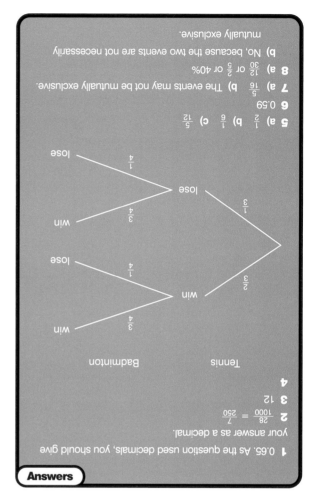

Answers

1 0.65. As the question used decimals, you should give your answer as a decimal.
2 $\frac{28}{1000} = \frac{7}{250}$
3 12
4
5 a) $\frac{1}{2}$ **b)** $\frac{1}{6}$ **c)** $\frac{5}{12}$
6 0.59
7 a) $\frac{5}{16}$ **b)** The events may not be mutually exclusive.
8 a) $\frac{12}{30}$ or $\frac{2}{5}$ or 40%
 b) No, because the two events are not necessarily mutually exclusive.

How did you get on?

All of them right?

You should be feeling really pleased with yourself, because almost all exam papers contain probability questions and you should score well here.

Most of them right, but one suit still dusty?

Note the suit which you need to brush up on.

Don't even ask?

The good news is that you are by no means alone. Many people start by hating probability. The even better news is that most people manage to learn it well enough to score highly in the exam, so don't give up on it. If you really have problems with probability, don't try to take in too many rules at one sitting. Do one suit and then have a change of topic.

Rules of probability

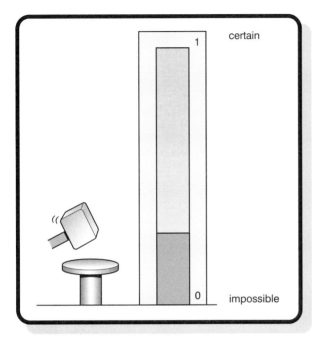

1. Each event's outcome can be assessed on a sliding scale from impossible to certain.

2. Impossible events have a probability of 0.

3. Certain events have a probability of 1.

4. All other possibilities are expressed as a fraction, decimal or percentage.

5. When all possible outcomes are added together, the total must be 1.

♣ Not let into the clubs? – numbers 1, 2, 7a) or 8a) wrong?

In most questions of probability:

OR means ADD

AND means MULTIPLY.

> ☾ **Madam Attix Says:**
> ☺ *You can remember that probability is a topic which you either adore (add–or), or you don't.*
> ✴

Solutions

1. In probability, an event always happens or it doesn't, and all the probabilities add up to 1. In this case you either win or you don't, so the probability of not winning is $1 - 0.35 = 0.65$.

2. Your chances of winning are 28 out of 1000. You always write probability as a fraction, decimal, or percentage, never using 'out of'. Note that $\frac{28}{1000}$ cancels down to $\frac{7}{250}$. If you have a calculator which has a fraction key, it is always a good idea to use it to check that you have cancelled adequately.

♦ Are your diamonds rough? Question 4 wrong?

Whether you are working with fractions or decimals, the probabilities branching from a common point always add up to 1.

♥ Weak hearts? Questions 3, 5 and 6 wrong?

To answer these questions, you need to know the and/or rules.

Whenever you can say 'and' you multiply the probabilities.

Usually you add when you can say 'or' but the next section tells you when this is wrong. If you have trouble remembering which goes with which, think of someone whom you add–or(e). What is the probability that they add–or(e) you?

> ☾ **Madam Attix Says:**
> ☺ If you can remember add–or(e), then
> ✴ 'and' goes with 'multiply'.

Solutions

3. There are six possible outcomes on a dice, and two on a coin, so you need all the outcomes on a dice **and** all those on a coin. $6 \times 2 = 12$

5. a) 'Wins both matches' can be written as, 'Wins the tennis **and** wins the badminton' so you multiply the probabilities.
   b) 'Wins the tennis, but not the badminton' would still make sense if it was written, 'Wins the tennis **and** not the badminton', so you can multiply the probabilities.

c) 'Wins only one tournament' means that he wins the tennis **and** not the badminton, **or** that he wins the badminton, **and** not the tennis. Once you have the probabilities associated with winning only one match and losing the other, you add them.

6 As you can only belong to one group at a time, you can add the probabilities. Circus members either join the acrobats or the custard-pie-dodgers. The probabilty is 0.59.

♠ Flattened by a spade? Question 7b) or 8b) wrong?

Sometimes **add** cannot be used for **or**. In question 6, you could add the probabilities, because members could belong to one and only one group. In this situation, events are said to be **mutually exclusive**. Events that do not influence each other are **independent**.

In question 7, it is not known whether some of the blue beads are also round, and if you simply add the probabilities, you might be counting some beads twice.

If you have a question of this type, where you are asked why you cannot add the probabilities, the answer is usually that the events are not mutually exclusive.

Solution

7 b) In probability, an event either happens, or it doesn't. Therefore, if you have worked out the probability of an event occurring, the probability of it not occurring is one minus the probability that it does occur.

Exercise 10.2

1 Delia Cardswright went to the fair and tried to win a prize on the coconut shy and at the hoopla stall. If the probability of winning a prize at the coconut shy was 0.15 and at the hoopla stall was 0.3, find the probability that she wins:
a) no prizes
b) a prize at hoopla but not at the coconut shy
c) exactly one prize
d) two prizes.
Hint: you may find a tree diagram helpful.

2 At the circus, 30% of the staff work with the animals, and 45% of the staff are women. Why might the probability of finding a female or a lion tamer not be 30% + 45% = 75%?

3 Delia Cardswright likes playing board games. She plays a game where two fair, six-sided dice are thrown simultaneously, and their scores are added together. Find the probability of her scoring:
a) 8　　**b)** 1　　**c)** 12.

4 a) Scarlett Rousers and Grace Ox make clothes together. If the probability of Scarlett producing a sub-standard item is 0.1 and that of Grace is 0.3, find the probability that both Scarlett and Grace make mistakes when producing a garment.
b) In a consignment of 900 garments, how many would you expect to have flaws from both?

5 The chart is an analysis of visitors to the fair one evening.

	under 20	20 or over
Men	210	350
Women	270	170

Using the table, find:
a) the probability that a visitor taken at random is a female aged 20 or over
b) the probability that a female visitor is under 20 years old
c) the probability that a male visitor is aged 20 or over. Give your answer as a fraction in its lowest terms.

6 Toby Onnottabee has drawn a diagram showing the possible routes out of the circus. Depending on which turn people take, they can pass points A, B, C or D.

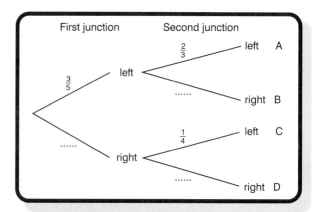

a) Complete the tree diagram.
b) Fay Lure is leaving the circus. Which point is she most likely to pass?
c) Which point is she least likely to pass?

review

How much have you learnt?

Tick off each topic in the list when you are confident you can cope with it.

- Find the probability of an event with a known number of possible outcomes.
- Find the joint probability of two events that are independent.
- Construct tree diagrams.
- Identify mutually exclusive events.
- Calculate the probability of two mutually exclusive events occurring.
- Comment on suggestions about the probabilities of two events that are not necessarily mutually exclusive.

Answers

1 a) 0.595 b) 0.255 c) 0.36 d) 0.045
2 The events are not mutually exclusive. There might be at least 1 female lion tamer.
3 a) $\frac{5}{36}$ b) 0 c) $\frac{1}{36}$
4 a) 0.03 b) 27
5 a) $\frac{17}{100}$ or 17% b) $\frac{27}{44}$ or 61% c) $\frac{5}{8}$
6 a)

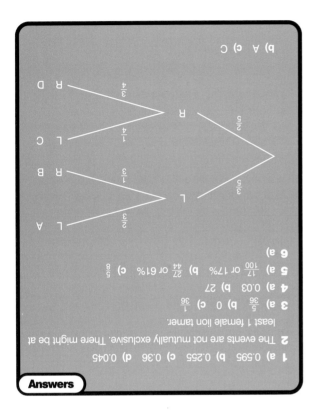

b) A c) C

When you have ticked off most of the items in the list above, and in the one at the end of Chapter 9, Statistics you can try the Handling data review, on page 134.

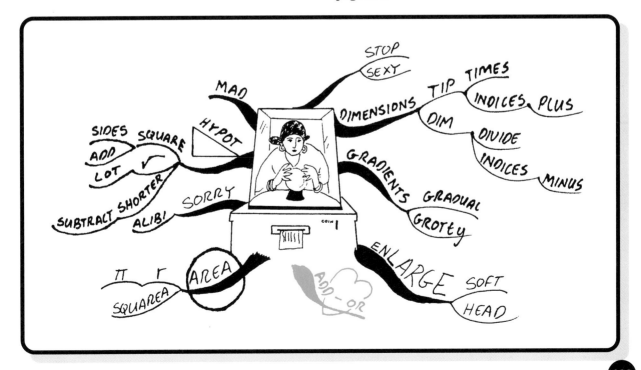

Handling data review

1 Find the mean, median and range for the following sets of data.
 a) 9.6, 10.1, 8.4, 9.8, 6.9, 11.4, 7.2
 b) 104, 116, 102, 14, 144, 100
 For the second set of data, which is a better measure of the average, the mean or the median? Give a reason for your answer.

2 In an experiment 30 plants were grown in a greenhouse. After two months their heights were recorded. The results are illustrated in the table below.

Height of plant (cm)	22	23	24	25	26	27	28
Frequency	1	0	3	6	9	11	0

 a) Find the mean, median, mode and range of the sample.
 b) At the same time, 30 similar plants were grown outdoors. The most common height was 24 cm. The range of heights was 8. Make two comparisons between the distributions.

3 An exam was sat by 40 people in class A. The percentage marks (x) scored are shown in the frequency table below.

Mark (x)	$0 < x \leqslant 20$	$20 < x \leqslant 40$	$40 < x \leqslant 60$
No. of students	8	21	6

Mark (x)	$60 < x \leqslant 80$	$80 < x \leqslant 100$
No. of students	3	2

 a) Calculate an estimate of the mean using mid-interval values.
 b) What is the modal class?
 c) **i)** Complete the cumulative frequency table below.

Mark (x)	$0 < x \leqslant 20$	$20 < x \leqslant 40$	$40 < x \leqslant 60$
Cumulative frequency			

Mark (x)	$60 < x \leqslant 80$	$80 < x \leqslant 100$
Cumulative frequency		

ii) On the axes below, draw a cumulative frequency curve to represent the given information.

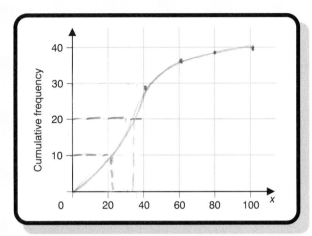

d) Find the median and the interquartile range.
e) Class B sat the same test. The median of their results was 60, and their interquartile range was 35.
  i) Which class had the higher average?
  ii) Which class was the more consistent?

4 In a survey 720 students were asked how they travelled to school. The results are as follows.

Type of transport	Frequency
On foot	108
By car	180
By bus	252
By train	36
By bicycle	144

a) Draw a pie chart to represent the above information.
b) What was the modal method of transport?
c) What percentage of students walked to school?

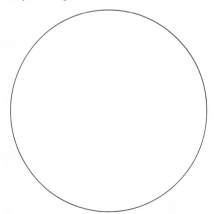

5 A school asked 100 boys and 100 girls how far they travelled to school. The results are given in the table below.

Distance from school (d km)	$0 < d \le 2$	$2 < d \le 4$	$4 < d \le 6$	$6 < d \le 8$
Boys	26	52	16	6
Girls	30	36	20	14

a) Draw two frequency polygons to represent this information, on the diagram below.

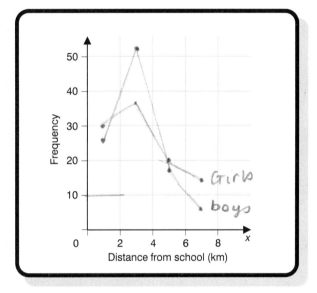

b) Name one similarity and one difference between the graphs.

Both have the same model point

The spread of the distance of girls is wider.

6 The size of engine, length and fuel consumption of ten cars were recorded. The results are illustrated in the two scatter diagrams below. Describe the correlations shown in the two diagrams.

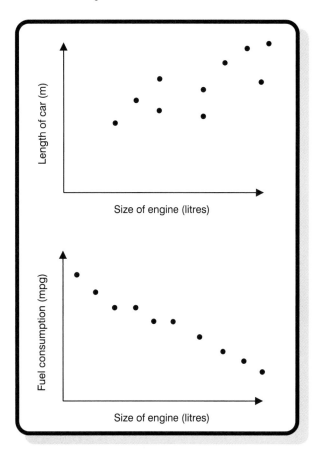

7 In a bag there are seven red, six green, two yellow and five blue marbles.
A marble is drawn, the colour noted and it is then replaced.
Giving your answer as a fraction in its lowest terms, find the probability that the marble is:

a) green   **b)** red or blue   **c)** not yellow.

8 A machine can develop either mechanical or electrical faults.
The probability of it developing a mechanical fault is 0.01, and an electrical fault 0.07.

a) What is the probability that it develops both types of fault?

b) How many machines would you expect to develop both faults out of a production line of 130 000?

9 In a class survey, 0.2 of the pupils were left-handed and 0.12 of them wore glasses.

a) What is the probability that a person picked at random is left-handed and wears glasses?

b) Why might it not be correct to say that the probability of a student being left-handed or wearing glasses is 0.32?

10 A test consist of two parts, A and B. It was found that 75% of the candidates pass A, but only 40% pass B.

a) Complete the tree diagram below.

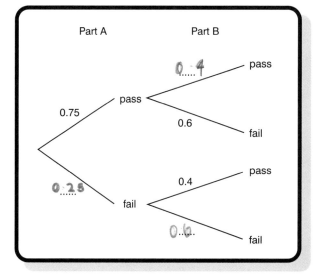

b) What percentage of the students pass both parts? 3 0

c) What percentage pass A or B but not both? 4 5 ⊦ 1 0

d) What percentage fail both parts? 15 %   5 5 · %

1 a) mean = 9.1, median = 9.6, range = 4.5

  b) mean = 96.7, median = 103 (It is the 3.5th
  number i.e. the average of 102 and 104.),
  range = 130
  The median is better as the mean is heavily influenced by
  the number 14.

2 a) mean = 25.8 cm, median (15.5th number) = 26 cm,
  mode = 27 cm
  range = 5 cm (Don't write your answer as 22 – 27!)

  b) The average/mode was higher for the plants grown in
  the greenhouse.
  The range/spread of heights was greater for those grown
  outdoors.

3 a) 35 **b)** $20 < x \leq 40$

  c) i)

Mark (x)	$0 < x \leq 20$	$20 < x \leq 40$	$40 < x \leq 60$
Cumulative frequency	8	29	35
Mark (x)	$60 < x \leq 80$	$80 < x \leq 100$	
Cumulative frequency	38	40	

  ii)

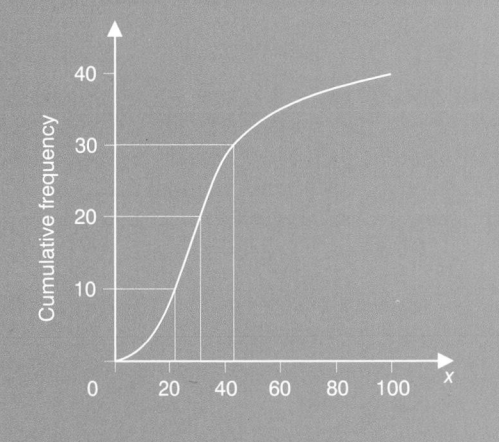

  d) 31, 21 approximately

  e) i) Class B **ii)** Class A

4 a) foot 54°, car 90°, bus 126°, train 18°, bicycle 72°

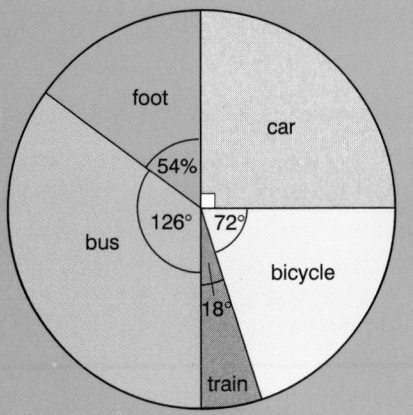

  b) bus **c)** 15%

5 a)

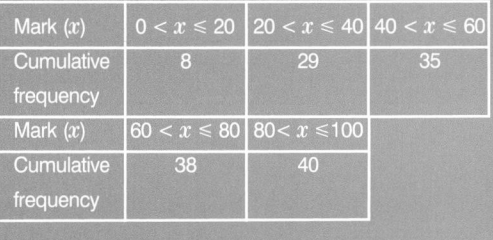

  b) Both have the same modal class.
  The spread of the distances for girls is wider.

6 a) weak positive **b)** strong negative

7 a) $\frac{3}{10}$ **b)** $\frac{3}{5}$ **c)** $\frac{9}{10}$

8 a) 0.0007 **b)** 91

9 a) 0.024 **b)** They are not mutually exclusive events.

10 a) Part A   Part B

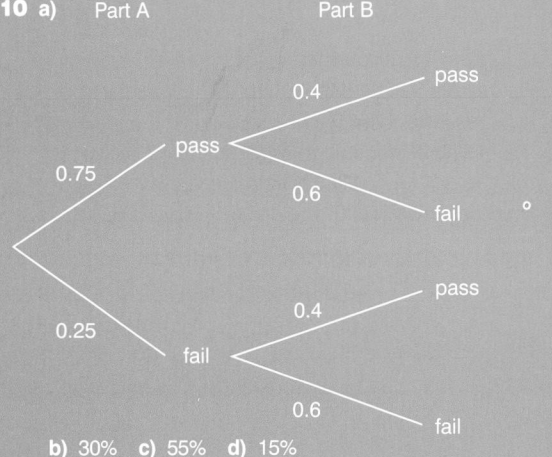

  b) 30% **c)** 55% **d)** 15%

Step-by-step revision

If you have a syllabus, you may find it rather daunting. Our three steps highlight the most important topics, i.e. those that crop up most often and that carry the most marks. Step 1 outlines an absolute minimum that you need to revise if you are to have any chance of achieving a C. If you can score highly on exam questions in these topics you will be well on the way to passing.

Step 1

Number

1   X-Direct

2   Use of calculator

3   Rounding and estimating

4   Standard form

Algebra

1   Substituting numbers into formulae

2   DINO and COSTAS

Shape and space

1   Area and circumference of a circle

2   Pythagoras' theorem and trigonometry

Handling data

1   Mean, median and mode

2   Probability

3   Surveys and samples

As you can see, this is a very short list. Look back in the book now if you are uncertain in any of these areas.

Step 2

These are the next most useful topics to revise. They may not appear quite as often as those in Step 1 but they still carry plenty of marks. Keep trying questions on the material from Step 1, though, while you are working through Step 2.

Number

1   Ratio ruler

2   Product of prime factors

Algebra

1   Equations, simple and simultaneous

2   Formula rearrangement

3   Simplifying and factorising

4   Gradient and equation of a line

Shape and space

1   Area and volume

2   Bearings

3   3D coordinates

4   Loci

5   Similar figures

6   Dimensions

Handling data

1   Frequency diagrams, especially cumulative frequency

2   Scatter diagrams and correlation

Step 3

If you have completed Step 2, congratulations! You are almost there. Look back at the chapter reviews and tick or highlight all of the topics with which you feel confident. There may still be a few items outstanding. Try to make time to fill these gaps because they could make all the difference between a D and a C, or a C and a B.

Checklist

Avoid these banana skins!

1 When do you plot a graph using end points?

2 What is the difference between significant figures and decimal places?

3 If you have n numbers, which one would be in the median position?

4 What do the interquartile range and range describe?

5 When shouldn't you use X-Direct?

6 When using Pythagoras' theorem and finding one of the shorter sides, what must you remember?

7 What three points should you remember when finding a bearing?

8 How many items of information must you remember to write for each of the four types of transformation?

9 a) In probability, what calculations do you associate with 'and' and 'or'?
   b) When must you be careful with using 'or'?

10 Give the formulae for the area and the circumference of a circle.

11 What should you check on your calculator before starting trigonometry?

12 How do you calculate the scale factor of an enlargement?

13 What should you remember when working in algebra with inequalities?

14 How do you find the mean of a grouped frequency?

15 What is the difference between using `SIN` and `INV SIN` on your calculator?

16 What shapes does the net of a cylinder consist of?

17 If a number has been rounded to the nearest 50, how would you find the smallest and largest values?

18 How do you know whether shapes tessellate?

19 What three letters can help you remember the rules for corresponding, opposite and alternate angles?

20 When is the mean an unsuitable measure of the average?

You may want to add some of your own banana skins at this point.

Here's a chance to try out all your new

Answers

1 Cumulative frequency

2 If you are unclear on this, turn to pages 15 – 16.

3 If n is even, the median is the mean of the $\frac{1}{2}n$th and the $\frac{1}{2}(n + 1)$th value. If n is odd, the median is the $\frac{1}{2}(n + 1)$th value.

4 How widely apart the data is spread.

5 Inverse proportion – it can drive you MAD!

6 For Shorter Sides Subtract.

7 Look north, turn clockwise, and always write the angle with three figures.

8 Reflection 1
  Translation 1
  Enlargement 2
  Rotation 3
  Look back to Chapter 8, Transformations, if you need to remind yourself about these points.

9 a) and = times, or = add
  b) When the events are not mutually exclusive.

10 area = πr^2, circumference = $2\pi r$ or πd

11 Check that it is set to degrees.

12 SOFT, Second Over First

13 The inequality reverses when you:
  a) swap the inequality around, or
  b) multiply or divide both sides by a negative number.

14 Start by finding the mid-interval values. See page 120 if you need more help.

15 Use sin if you want to find a length, use inv sin if you have the sine and want to find an angle.

16 Two circles and a rectangle

17 Halve 50 to make 25, then add it to the given number to make the largest, and subtract it to make the smallest.

18 The angles around the common point should total 360°.

19 F, X and Z respectively

20 When a small part of the sample is much bigger or

Specimen examination papers

Here's a chance to try out all your new skills on two practice papers. We have tried to make them as close to the real thing as possible, but all examiners have their own funny little ways, so it is a good idea to do as many past papers as possible. No doubt your Maths teacher will keep you busy.

Before you start on Paper 1, though, Ringo has a few hints to help you avoid that awful sinking feeling.

1 Work right through the paper, doing as many questions as you can. Leave out any questions you can't do straight away, then come back to them.

2 If you are working on a question and you get a sudden brainwave about another question, jot it down somewhere (perhaps the inside cover) to use later.

3 A lucky guess might gain you some marks. A blank page never does. If you attempt at least part of a question, there is a chance that you will get some marks.

4 Don't get bogged down in any one question. It's better to move on and come back later if you have time.

5 Always show your working. It's surprising how many marks you can pick up, even if you get the wrong answer.

And finally, if you really don't know where to start, remember:

Read the question.
Identify the problem, i.e. what are they asking?
Note the information, i.e. what do I know already, what information are they giving me?
Get on with it.
Or go back and attempt the question again later if you have time.

Paper 1

1 In a sale, a shop reduced all its prices by 15%.
  a) Find the new price of an article which originally cost £55.00.
  b) Find the original price if the reduced price is £102.
  c) In the week before the sale, the average number of customers per day was 250. During the sale this number increased to 370. What was the percentage increase?

2 Solve the following equations.
  a) $10x + 3 = 12x - 7$
  b) $4x + 2 = 2x - 12$
  c) $4(x - 3) = 2 - x$
  d) Use an algebraic method to solve the following simultaneous equations.
  $5x + 2y = 29$
  $2x + 5y = 41$

3 a) The following table gives some values for the equation $y = 2x - 4$. Fill in the rest of the table.

x	-2	-1	0	1	2	3	4
y	-8			-2		2	

  b) Taking values of x between -2 and 4, and values of y between -8 and 4, draw the graph of $y = 2x - 4$.
  c) Hence or otherwise, find the gradient and the y-intercept.

4 Find the angle marked x below, to the nearest degree.

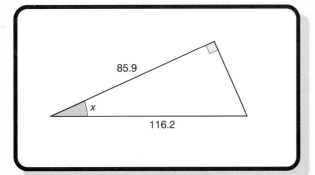

5 ABCDEFGH (at the top of the next column) is a regular octagon centred at O.
Find the size of:
  a) angle BCD
  b) angle BED
  c) angle ABE
  d) What name is given to the shape BCDE?
  e) What is the order of symmetry of the octagon?

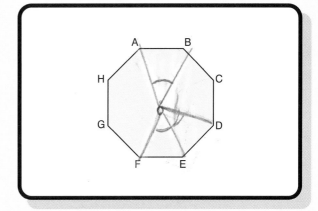

6 i) In the sequence, 15, 19, 23, 27, ... give:
      a) the next two terms   **b)** the 20th term
      c) the nth term.
  ii) A sequence is made by doubling the previous term and subtracting 2. Give the next three terms.
      3, 4, 6, 10, ...
  iii) Give the next term and a formula for finding the nth term.
      4, 7, 12, 19, ...

7 A fish tank is made in the shape of a cuboid. with a base measuring 60 cm by 40 cm. If it contains 72 litres of water, how deep is the water in the tank?

8 i) Simplify where possible.
      a) $3(2x + y) - (x - y)$
      b) $5x^2 + 2x + 7x + 2y + y^2$
  ii) Find the solutions to these equations.
      a) $(x - 3)(x + 2) = 0$
      b) $x^2 + 8x + 7 = 0$
      c) $x^2 - 8x - 20 = 0$

9 A survey, carried out on the ages of 80 members of a sports' club, gave the following information.

No. of years, x	Frequency	Cumulative frequency
Less than 10	2	
$10 < x \leq 20$	16	
$20 < x \leq 30$	30	
$30 < x \leq 40$	16	
$40 < x \leq 50$	10	
$50 < x \leq 60$	6	

  a) Complete the column showing the cumulative frequency.

b) Draw a cumulative frequency graph, and use it to find the median and the interquartile range.

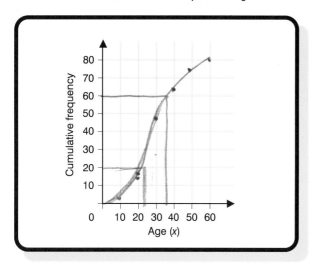

c) Using the information given in the table above, state the modal group, and find an estimate of the mean.

10 'Don't you agree that there aren't enough programmes for teenagers on TV?'
Is this a good question to ask when conducting a survey in teenagers' viewing habits?
Give a reason for your answer.

11 A rectangular garden, ABCD, has dimensions AB = CD = 20 m, BC = AD = 14 m. AB is the back wall of a house.
a) Make an accurate scale drawing of the garden, using a scale of 0.5 cm to 1 m. How long should AB be on the plan?
b) A tree is to be planted 6 m from the house and equidistant from AD and CD. Using a ruler and compasses only, mark the spot T where the tree is to be planted.
c) A pond is to be made so that it is to be no more than 13 m from both A and C. Indicate the region where it is to be dug.

12 Match the labels to the graphs below.
a) $y = x^3$ **b)** $y = -x$
c) $y = x^2 + 2$ **d)** $y = 2x - 3$

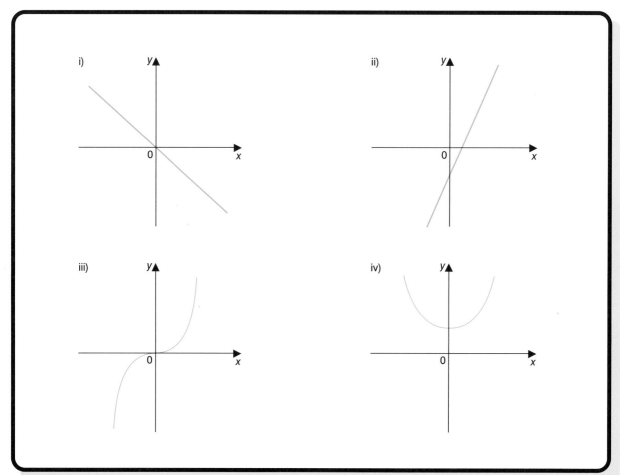

1 a) £46.75 **b)** £120.00 **c)** 48%

2 a) $x = 5$ **b)** $x = -7$ **c)** $x = 2.8$ **d)** $x = 3, y = 7$

3 a)

x	–2	–1	0	1	2	3	4
y	–8	–6	–4	–2	0	2	4

b)

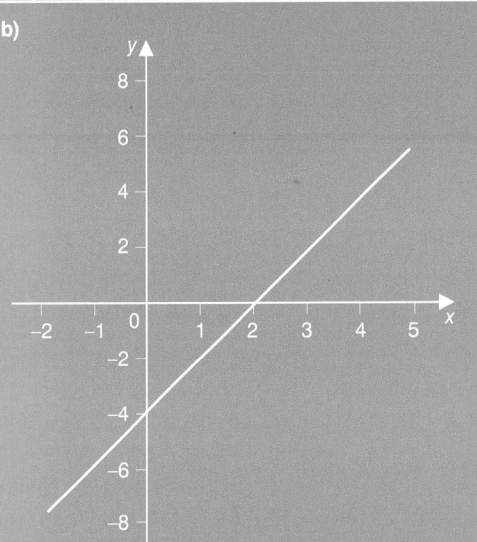

c) gradient = 2, y-intercept = –4

4 42°

5 a) 135° **b)** 45° **c)** 90° **d)** trapezium
   e) Order 8 or 8-fold rotational symmetry

6 i) a) 31, 35 **b)** 91 **c)** $4n + 11$
   ii) 18, 34, 66
   iii) 28, $n^2 + 3$

7 30 cm

8 i) a) $5x + 4y$ **b)** $5x^2 + 9x + 2y + y^2$
   ii) a) $x = 3, x = -2$ **b)** $x = -7, x = -1$
      c) $x = 10, x = -2$

9 a)

No. of years, x	Frequency	Cumulative frequency
Less than 10	2	2
$10 < x \leq 20$	16	18
$20 < x \leq 30$	30	48
$30 < x \leq 40$	16	64
$40 < x \leq 50$	10	74
$50 < x \leq 60$	6	80

b) median = 27, IQR = 16

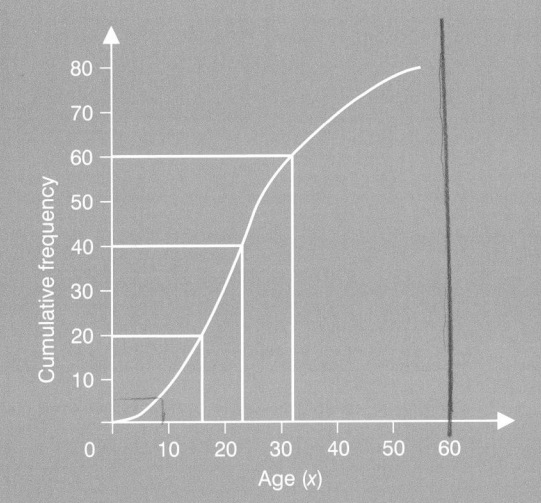

c) $20 < x \leq 30$, mean = 29.25

10 This is a bad question, because it is leading, i.e. it is suggesting a particular response to the interviewee.

11 a) 10 cm

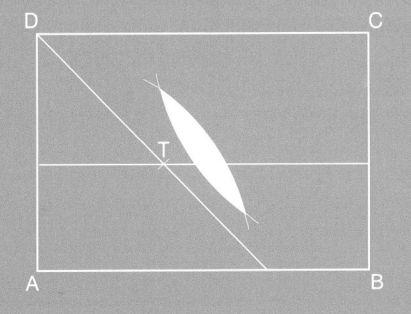

12 a) (iii) **b)** (i) **c)** (iv) **d)** (ii)

Paper 2

1 1 litre is approximately equal to 1.75 pints and 8 pints make 1 gallon.
  a) How many gallons are approximately equal to 40 litres?
  b) How many litres are approximately equal to 15.75 gallons?

2 a) The probability of a student taking French is 0.3 and of taking German is 0.4. What is the probability that a student takes German but not French?
  b) The probability of a girl being picked for the girls' netball team is 0.4. The probability of a boy being picked for the boys' rugby team is 0.3. The probability of a student being picked for the school chess team is 0.2.
    i) Why might it be incorrect to say that the probability of being chosen for either the netball or the chess team is 0.4 + 0.2?
    ii) What further information would you need to be able to estimate the probability of being chosen for either the netball or the chess team?

3 An employer advertised a part-time job at the rate of £50.00 per week plus £5.75 per hour.
  a) If w stands for the wage in pounds, and h stands for hours worked, write a formula in terms of w and h to show this information.
    Begin the formula: $w =$
  b) Rearrange the formula to make h the subject.
  c) If an employee earned £165.00 in a week, how many hours would have been worked?

4 A millionaire is estimated to be worth £22 000 000 to the nearest million. What is the lower bound of his wealth?

5 A cylinder has a base radius of 1.7 m, and a height of 3.4 m.
  a) Find its volume.
  b) Find its surface area.

6 i) Using a calculator, work out the following. Give your answers in standard form correct to 3 significant figures.
    a) $(3.7 \times 10^8) \times (1.4 \times 10^4)$
    b) $(8.6 \times 10^{12}) \div (3.2 \times 10^5)$

  ii) Use a calculator to work out the following examples. Give your answers correct to 1 decimal place.
    a) $\dfrac{3.7 + 9.2}{1.4 \times \sqrt{0.16}}$ **b)** $\dfrac{\sqrt{17 \times 3.7^2}}{12.6 - 2.5}$ **c)** $\dfrac{2.1^2 + 15.8}{7.1 - 2.2}$
    d) Without using a calculator, show how you can give a rough estimate of the answer to:
    $\dfrac{2.1^2 + 15.8}{7.1 - 2.2}$

7 In the diagram below calculate:
  a) AB   **b)** BC   **c)** the area of triangle ACD.

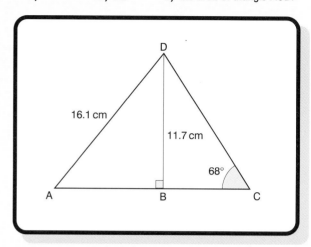

8 You are given that l, h and r are all lengths. Using dimensions, state with a reason whether each of the following is a formula for length, area, volume or none of these.
  a) $\pi r^2 + 2lh + r^3$ **b)** $4l(h + r)$
  c) $4h + \frac{1}{4}\pi r + \frac{1}{2}l$ **d)** $\pi r^2(l + h)$ **e)** $\frac{4}{3}\pi r^3 \div h$

9 Describe fully the transformation which maps:
  a) P on to Q   **b)** P to R   **c)** P to S.

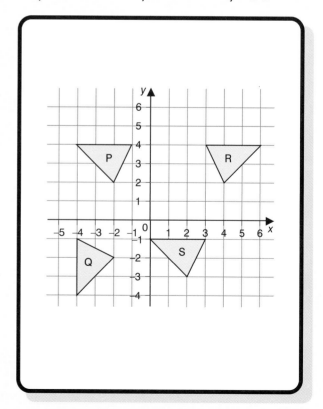

10 a) Express 780 as a product of its prime factors.
b) $18\,000 = 2^x \times 3^y \times 5^z$. Find x, y and z.

11 On the diagram below, shade the region indicated by the following inequalities.
$x \leqslant 3$
$y \geqslant 1$
$y \leqslant x$

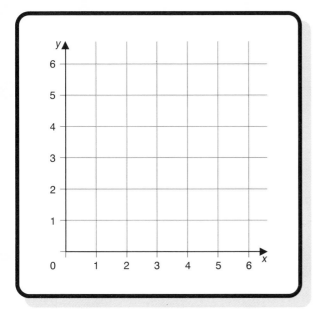

12 Find:
a) the mean   **b)** the median   **c)** the range
of these numbers.
7, 8, 3, 9, 6, 30
d) Is the mean or the median a better indicator of the average? Give a reason.

Answers

1 a) 8.75 gallons   **b)** 72 litres

2 a) 0.28
b) i) The probabilities are not mutually exclusive.
ii) You would need to know how many girls are in both groups.

3 a) $u = 50 + 5.75h$ **b)** $h = \dfrac{u - 50}{5.75}$ **c)** 20 hours

4 £21 500 000 or £21.5 million

5 a) $30.9\,m^2$ **b)** $54.5\,m^2$

6 i) a) 5.18×10^{12} **b)** 2.69×10^7
ii) a) 23.0   **b)** 1.5   **c)** 4.1
d) $4 + 16 = 20$, $7 - 2 = 5$, $20 \div 5 = 4$

7 a) 11.1 cm   **b)** 4.7 cm   **c)** $92.4\,cm^2$

8 a) none (area + area + volume)
b) area (length × length)
c) length (length + length + length)
d) volume (length² × length = length × length × length)
e) area (volume ÷ length = area)

9 a) rotation anti-clockwise, 90°, centre (0, 0)
b) reflection in the line $x = 1$
c) translation $\begin{pmatrix} 4 \\ -5 \end{pmatrix}$

10 a) $780 = 2^2 \times 3 \times 5 \times 13$
b) $x = 4$, $y = 2$, $z = 3$

11

12 a) mean = 10.5, median = 7.5, range = 27
b) The median is better, as the mean is distorted by the one much larger value.

147

Index